Verbal Reasoning:
Comprehension

For the CEM (Durham University) test

11+
Comprehension

Ages
10-11

The
10-Minute Test
Answer Book

Book 2

Practise • Prepare • Pass
Everything your child needs for 11+ success

Test 1 — pages 2-5

1. D

The seaside is described as "just a thought" (line 4) to the narrator, which could suggest that it only exists in their imagination or their memories. That the narrator had a "home upon the sea" (line 6) shows that they have real experiences of the sea, but that this was a long time ago and it is only a memory now.

2. B

Lines 9-10 state that the narrator's "favourite things were a decent wind / And the sight of millpond seas". "decent" can mean 'satisfactory' and a millpond is an incredibly calm body of water. This shows that the narrator liked a fair amount of wind and calm seas as a child.

3. A

"simple" can mean 'basic' and 'uncomplicated'. Since the narrator describes life at sea as a "simple life of ease" (line 12), it can be inferred that they think life at sea is untroubled and uncomplicated.

4. D

In lines 14-15, the narrator states that they now live in "Tall cities without end" and that they "live in a silent flat of stone". This shows that they live in a flat in a large city.

5. A

In line 18, the narrator refers to the sea as their "sapphire friend". Lines 19-24 go on to describe the "whitened paws" of this "friend" "skirting along the land". Therefore, the "whitened paws" refer to waves lapping up onto the shore.

6. A

In line 25, the narrator states they wish to travel "far beyond the coast", so will leave the land behind. Therefore, we can infer that the giant cliffs appear as "but a line" because they are very far away.

7. C

The narrator states that they will be "Aboard" their "floating shrine" (line 30). 'aboard' often refers to being on a boat. Since the narrator is describing being at sea, we can infer that the "floating shrine" is a boat.

8. B

In line 31, the narrator states "I'll care not where it is I'm swept", implying that they won't mind where they sail to once they are on the sea.

9. C

Line 29 describes the sea as "sunlit", implying the weather is sunny. Line 34 describes the sea as a "thunderous fray". "thunderous" means 'relating to thunder', implying the sea is rough due to storms. Line 35 describes "cotton clouds as black as pitch", showing the weather is overcast. There is no mention of rain in the poem.

10. B

The narrator states that, when they face "eternal sleep" (line 38), they wish to "stay upon the endless sea, / At rest in his blue embrace" (lines 41-42). "eternal sleep" refers to death, suggesting that, when it is time for the narrator to die, they hope to be put to rest at sea.

11. D

"caresses" and 'strokes' both mean 'to touch gently'.

12. A

"eternal" and 'endless' both mean 'lasting forever'.

Test 2 — pages 6-9

1. D

Line 2 states that the role of hospital trains was to enable "wounded soldiers to be evacuated from war zones". "evacuated" means 'taken away from danger'.

2. B

Lines 4-5 state that the Grand Crimean Central Railway was built "so that trains laden with ammunition and food could be used to supply the British army and its allies".

3. D

Lines 10-11 state that, for World War I and World War II, "Britain's fleet of hospital trains was expanded", showing that there were more hospital trains in use during World War II than during the Crimean War, which happened earlier, in the mid-19th century (line 3).

4. A

Line 16 states that hospital trains used in World War II featured a "pharmacy", which is another word for a medicine store. Lines 16-17 state that there were "dedicated mess areas, where chefs would cook for staff and passengers", showing that there must have been kitchens. Lines 22-23 state that "staff lived aboard the train" and slept "in confined quarters". There is no mention of an artillery store.

5. C

The fact that staff had to "work through the night to fulfil their duties" (line 19) implies that they needed to work both night and day to ensure their work was carried out. Since their work was focused on caring for the patients, we can infer that the patients needed to be cared for during both the day and the night.

6. A

Orderlies were responsible for "changing dressings and feeding the patients" (lines 20-21). The train had onboard chefs (line 17) and orderlies were only involved in assisting medical staff in "basic tasks" (line 20), so orderlies wouldn't have been expected to cook for staff or perform operations.

7. B

If something is described as being in 'the line of fire', it means that it is in danger of being hit by gunfire or missiles.

8. B

'perilous' means 'dangerous', 'fetid' means 'very smelly' and 'cramped' can mean 'crowded'. Line 22 states that staff worked "in the line of fire" and line 23 describes the hospital trains as "smelly and crowded". There is no mention of the trains being mouldy.

9. C

Lines 10-12 states that "normal passenger trains were stripped of their seats and modified" to make hospital trains during World War I and World War II. Line 13 states that World War II hospital trains were "14 carriages" long. Line 14 states that the hospital trains during World War II were capable of carrying "around 360 patients". There is no mention of how many staff worked on hospital trains.

10. D

Lines 24-25 state that "patients were initially relieved to board a hospital train", showing that they viewed them positively before boarding them. Lines 25-26 state that the "harsh reality on board meant many were thankful when the journey was over", showing that the train was not as pleasant to travel on as they had hoped.

2

11. B

"rudimentary" and 'crude' can both mean 'basic'.

12. A

"confined" and 'restricted' can both mean 'lacking in space'.

Test 3 — pages 10-13

1. C

In line 2, the narrator states that he first tried to come up with a way to start his story by "scratching" his head. "scratching your head" is a way of saying 'pondering', which shows he is trying to think of his own way to start the story.

2. D

Line 5 states that Penelope thinks the story should begin "with the day when we got the news that Mr. Franklin Blake was expected".

3. A

Lines 11-12 state that Penelope's journal "is for her own private eye, and that no living creature shall ever know what is in it but herself", showing that there are things she has written in the diary that she wishes no one to see.

4. A

Line 20 states that the narrator hasn't seen Franklin "since he was a boy" which implies he hasn't seen Franklin for a long time.

5. B

The narrator receives news of Mr. Franklin's arrival on the 24th May (line 15). Line 18 states that Mr. Franklin intends to stay "till next month" to "keep Rachel's birthday". Therefore, Rachel's birthday must fall within a month of 24th May, which means it can only be in either May or June.

6. D

'indefinitely' can mean 'for an unlimited length of time'. Mr. Franklin will stop at the house "till next month" (line 18), implying that he is only planning to stay temporarily.

7. C

Throwing a hat up into the air can be a sign of celebration. Since the narrator has just received news of Mr. Franklin's impending arrival (lines 16-18), it can be inferred that his excitement is related to this news.

8. A

Lines 2-3 state that Penelope is the narrator's daughter. Line 15 states that the story the narrator is writing begins in "Eighteen hundred and forty-eight" (i.e. 1848). Line 16 shows that the narrator is called Gabriel, since this is how he is addressed by his employer. There is no mention of where the house is in relation to London.

9. A

In lines 21-22, the narrator describes Mr. Franklin as "the nicest boy that ever spun a top". A 'top' is a type of children's toy, so this suggests that the narrator remembers Mr. Franklin as a playful child. The narrator also implies that Mr. Franklin "broke a window" (line 22), suggesting that he was mischievous and sometimes caused trouble as a child.

10. C

If something is described as 'objectionable', it means that it is 'unpleasant'. In Line 24, Rachel describes Mr. Franklin as "atrocious", which can mean 'very wicked'. This shows that Rachel thought Mr. Franklin's conduct was disagreeable.

11. B

"devised" and 'conceived' both mean 'thought up'.

12. A

"tyrant" and 'bully' mean 'someone who intimidates others'.

Puzzles 1 — page 14

Pony Club Problems

1st Place: Pickles, Serena, Yellow
2nd Place: Bullseye, Harriet, Green
3rd Place: Jupiter, Benjamin, Red
4th Place: Dasher, Jack, Blue

Test 4 — pages 15-18

1. C

If someone moves 'at a bound' then they are moving quickly by taking big strides.

2. B

"reckoned upon" and 'anticipated' both mean 'expected'. In this part of the passage, d'Artagnan is anticipating that he will be able to take the steps four at a time.

3. D

In line 7, Athos questions d'Artagnan's treatment of him after he has bumped into him by saying: "You say, 'Excuse me,' and you believe that is sufficient?". This suggests that Athos isn't satisfied with d'Artagnan's account of himself and wants to continue speaking with him.

4. A

Turning pale can be associated with anger. In lines 6-9, Athos takes issue with d'Artagnan's behaviour, suggesting that he is angry with him and that this is the reason he has turned pale.

5. D

In lines 7-9, Athos says to d'Artagnan, "Do you fancy because you have heard Monsieur de Treville speak to us a little cavalierly today that other people are to treat us as he speaks to us?". This suggests that he won't allow d'Artagnan to speak to him in the same offhand way that Monsieur de Treville has done, without being reprimanded.

6. A

In line 10, d'Artagnan says, "I did not do it intentionally", showing that he didn't deliberately run into Athos and that he didn't mean to annoy him.

7. B

In lines 12-13, Athos says to d'Artagnan "you are not polite; it is easy to perceive that you come from a distance", suggesting that Athos thinks d'Artagnan's is rude because he comes from somewhere far away where people are less well-mannered.

8. A

In lines 12-13, Athos says that d'Artagnan is "not polite" and then implies that it's because he comes "from a distance". D'Artagnan stops "at Athos's last remark" (line 14), suggesting that he dislikes Athos's comment about where he comes from.

9. C

In line 17, d'Artagnan says that he is "running after someone". Lines 22-23 state that d'Artagnan is trying to find a "stranger, whose slow pace could not have carried him far", suggesting that he wants to catch up with them.

10. A

In lines 18-21, d'Artagnan agrees to have a duel with Athos, suggesting that he does want to retaliate.

11. C

In line 21, d'Artagnan says "I will be there ten minutes before twelve". Here, d'Artagnan is showing that he is so eager to turn up to the duel and fight Athos that he plans to arrive early.

12. B

"endeavouring" and 'striving' both mean 'trying'.

Test 5 — pages 19-22

1.   D
Lines 7-9 state that 46 years after 1960, *Trace* was installed. This must have been in 2006. Line 3 states that the Hampton Court maze was built "around 1691", so the maze must have been approximately 2006 – 1691 = 315 years old when *Trace* was introduced.

2.   B
Lines 10-14 describe the mazes at Longleat. Lines 12-13 state that "Visitors to this stately home and estate" can also enjoy King Arthur's Mirror Maze, implying that Longleat is the site of a manor house with grounds that are open to visitors.

3.   C
Line 18 states that the labyrinth at Chatres Cathedral is "made from tiles". Line 21 states that the labyrinth at St Paul's Cathedral was "painted on canvas". Line 23 describes how labyrinths, such as the one at Saffron Walden, are cut into "lawned areas", implying they are made of grass. The passage contains examples of mazes made using trees, but no labyrinths.

4.   B
Line 5 states that Hampton Court maze has "half a mile of paths". Line 12 states that Longleat has "1.5 miles of path". 3 × 0.5 = 1.5, so the maze at Longleat is 3 times as long as the maze at Hampton Court.

5.   C
Lines 5-6 state that the maze at Hampton Court is "one of the most popular mazes in the world", so it is not 'obsolete', which means 'fallen into disuse'.

6.   D
Line 25 states the diameter of the largest turf labyrinth in Britain, but does not state the area that it covers.

7.   C
Lines 1-2 state that mazes "offer a series of bewildering choices, forcing those who enter to select the correct route to the centre". Lines 15-16 state that labyrinths have "a single route" that visitors "merely have to follow". Therefore, no decision-making is required when tackling a labyrinth.

8.   B
Lines 24-25 state that Saffron Walden is the largest turf labyrinth in Britain and that it has a 132-foot diameter. Therefore, most turf labyrinths must have a smaller diameter than this.

9.   D
Lines 4-5 state that the maze at Hampton Court is "the world's oldest hedge maze", so the hedge maze at Longleat must have been built more recently than "around 1691" (line 3). Lines 24-25 state that the turf maze at Saffron Walden was built "in the late 1600s". Line 17 states that the labyrinth at Chatres Cathedral is a "13th-century labyrinth", so was built sometime between 1200-1300 AD, making it the oldest.

10.   A
Line 8 states that the hedges of the maze at Hampton Court Palace were "replaced by yew trees". Line 12 states that the hedge maze at Longleat consists of paths that are "flanked by yew trees", meaning they both feature walls made of the same material.

11.   C
Lines 20-21 state that the labyrinth at St Paul's Cathedral was "temporary", implying that it is not still there.

12.   A
Line 5 states that the maze at Hampton Court has "half a mile of paths". Line 12 states that the hedge maze at Longleat has "1.5 miles of path". Line 18 states that the pathway of the labyrinth is 260 metres long. Line 25 states that Saffron Walden turf labyrinth has a "mile-long pathway". Therefore, the hedge maze at Longleat has the longest distance of paths.

Puzzles 2 — page 23

Stepping Stone Maze

The correct words are: **KERNEL, BULLSEYE, HUB, MIDDLE, HEART, EYE, MIDPOINT, CORE**

Test 6 — pages 24-27

1.   B
Line 2 states that sign languages involve "hand gestures". Lines 3-4 state that other key parts of sign languages include "facial expressions" and "fingerspelling". There is no mention of blinking being part of sign language.

2.   A
Line 11 states that Watson developed and advocated "the combined system", not BSL itself.

3.   B
Line 8 states that the combined system was a "predecessor of British Sign Language". "predecessor" and 'forerunner' both mean 'precursor'.

4.   B
Lines 12-14 state that there was "ignorance about the values of a formal sign language" and that the use of signing was "actively discouraged", showing that people were unaware of the usefulness of signing.

5.   D
'collaborative' means 'made by people who work together'. Lines 15-17 state that BSL "had been developing in deaf communities over time and had started to be formalised in the 'combined system'", suggesting that a variety of people came together to create BSL.

6.   B
Line 18 states that BSL was recognised as a formal language in 2003, which is under 50 years ago.

7.   C
Line 17 states that BSL began to be "taken more seriously as a language" from the 1970s, showing that people began to see BSL as a valid way to communicate.

8.   A
Line 8 states that the combined system was "the predecessor of British Sign Language". Lines 25-26 state that "Auslan... and New Zealand Sign Language are closely related to BSL".

9.   D
America is an English-speaking country, but line 21 states that it uses "American Sign Language".

10.   B
The phrase "variants of verbal languages" (line 23) is used to define regional "dialects" (line 23) of spoken languages.

11.   B
"components" and 'elements' both mean 'parts of a whole'.

12.   A
"divergences" and 'deviations' both mean 'moving away from something that is considered normal'.

Test 7 — pages 28-31

1. D
The Havoc is described as a "twisting warren" (line 3) and line 4 states that Anya found it "bewildering". This suggests that it was hard to navigate. 'disorientating' describes something that is hard to navigate.

2. B
That Anya knows the Havoc just "as well as" she knows her own streets (line 7) means that she is as familiar with the streets of the Havoc as she is with the streets that she actually lives on, showing that Anya does not live in the Havoc.

3. C
Line 8 states "the sun slipped below the horizon just as Anya arrived at the Inventor's house". The time just after sunset when the sun is no longer visible is called 'dusk'.

4. D
The Inventor's house is in the Havoc, which is "occupied by the poorest citizens" (line 3). In line 11, the narrator says that Anya doesn't know how the Inventor is able to afford a fire "given his address", suggesting that Anya's surprise is related to the fact that the Inventor lives in a poor area.

5. A
In line 17, the Inventor impatiently asks Anya where she has been, suggesting that he has been waiting for her. He then says "I need to show you something" (lines 17-18), before leading Anya to the invention, suggesting that he chastised Anya because he had been waiting to show her the invention.

6. B
The invention is described as "gleaming" (line 19). The words 'lustrous' and "gleaming" both mean 'shining'.

7. A
The word "palpable" describes a feeling so strong it can almost be seen or touched. Anya "couldn't help but be infected" (line 20) by the Inventor's excitement, showing that she could almost physically feel the Inventor's excitement.

8. D
Lines 21-22 state that the invention "had been his obsession for as long as she'd known him", but the exact amount of time it took for the Inventor to complete his invention is not given.

9. C
Lines 22-23 state that when Anya inspects the invention, she notices that it looks "exactly the same as it had the previous day, though a narrow spindle now protruded from its centre". This shows that Anya knows the invention well enough to be able to tell whether anything is different.

10. B
In line 27, the Inventor tells Anya that the invention is finished and "sighed, finally at ease". This suggests that he is relieved that he is free from the burden of working on the invention.

11. B
"ensconced" and 'settled' both mean 'to be comfortably established somewhere'.

12. A
"protruded" and 'projected' both mean 'stuck out from something'.

Test 8 — pages 32-35

1. D
The word 'austere' can mean 'undecorated'. Lines 1-2 state that "not even a sea flower grew to relieve the stern grandeur of this vast corridor". This suggests that the corridor is not adorned with anything.

2. C
Line 5 states that Trot is "at the bottom of the great ocean, swimming through a big tunnel", showing the corridor is under the sea.

3. B
To become "impressed" with something can mean 'to become aware of' or 'to realise the importance of something'. In lines 2-3, Trot has started to think about her situation and she wonders whether "she would ever get back again to the white cottage on the cliff" (line 4) that is her home, suggesting that she has now become aware of how far away it is.

4. C
Line 6 states that there is "a group of horrible sea devils" at the other end of the tunnel. Line 20 states that there was "no escaping the sea devils behind them", showing that the party was being forced to swim through the tunnel.

5. A
Lines 8-10 state that Trot relied "more upon her tried and true friend, Cap'n Bill, than upon her newer acquaintances to see her safely out of her present trouble". The "newer acquaintances" Trot refers to are the fairy mermaids, Aquareine and Clia. Therefore, this means that Trot believes that Cap'n Bill is the one who will protect her from harm.

6. D
Line 9 describes the two fairies, Aquareine and Clia, as "newer acquaintances" compared to Cap'n Bill, showing that she has known Bill for longer. In lines 12-13, Cap'n Bill says he doesn't care about himself but that he is "drea'ful worried over our Trot", suggesting that he feels responsible for looking our for her and that he cares more about her safety than he does his own.

7. D
To speak in a "low voice" can mean to speak quietly. This suggests that Cap'n Bill only wants Clia to hear him.

8. A
In lines 16-17, Clia says "Trust to our powerful queen, and be sure she will find some means for us all to escape uninjured." This shows that Clia is loyal because she has faith in Aquareine and trusts she will make the right decisions.

9. C
In line 21, Aquareine decides that the best way to get out of their situation is to go through the archway and "bravely face the unknown Zog", suggesting that she knows Zog is likely to be somewhere beyond the archway.

10. B
Line 23 states that Aquareine "led the way" through the archway after deciding that they should go through it. This suggests she is in charge as she is leading the party forwards.

11. A
"reigned" and 'prevailed' can both mean 'dominated'.

12. D
"relieve" and 'soften' can both mean 'lessen the intensity of something'.

Puzzles 3 — page 36

Dastardly Directions
The directions with mistakes are: 1, 4, 6, 7 and 9

The mistakes are:
Direction 1: 'rout' (route), 'gait' (gate)
Direction 4: 'passed' (past), 'entrance' (enter)
Direction 6: 'strait' (straight), 'folowing' (following), 'untill' (until)
Direction 7: 'off' (of), 'streem' (stream)
Direction 9: 'over' (other), 'littel' (little)

The correct route is shown by the black line below.

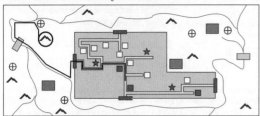

Test 9 — pages 37-40

1. D
Line 3 states that Mateo is performing at the "250th Summer Festival". Line 7 states that the "first annual Summer Festival" occurred in 1768, so the year in which Mateo is performing must be 249 years later (in 2017). Lines 12-14 state that, while Mateo was rehearsing on the day of the concert, there was "hot August weather", showing that the month must be August.

2. C
Line 1 states that there was a "5000-strong audience" in the Opera House. Line 5 states that this "was just over double the size of the crowd" at Mateo's Reitzen Theatre concert. Half of the Opera House crowd is 2500, so the Reitzen crowd must have been just under 2500 people.

3. A
Line 11 states that Mateo studied "abroad in Filben". "abroad" means 'in a different country', showing that the Filben is not in Salburn. Line 16 describes Carla Piento as Mateo's "fellow Filben Conservatoire graduate", implying that this is the place where Mateo studied "abroad".

4. A
Line 2 states that Mateo is making "his debut at Salburn's most prestigious venue". This venue is named as the "Salene Opera House" (line 17). 'debut' means 'first appearance'. Therefore, Mateo cannot have performed at the Salene Opera House before.

5. B
Lines 19-20 state that, when Carla Piento asked the question "Pronto?", Mateo "nodded in response, but he did not feel ready at all". This implies that Carla is asking Mateo if he is ready.

6. D
Lines 9-10 state that there was a "recital of Handel's Messiah at the Vienno Cathedral", showing that there are other venues that host musical performances during the Summer Festival.

7. C
'to know the ropes' means 'to have experience'. Lines 16-17 state that Carla Piento was a "seasoned performer in the Salene Opera House", implying that she has lots of experience performing at the Salene Opera House.

8. B
Line 1 states that the Salene Opera House has a "domed roof", a type of vaulted roof. Line 15 states that there are also "boxes in the hall" for spectators. Line 25 states that Mateo "walked onto the stage". There is no mention of private practice rooms in the Salene Opera House.

9. A
Line 23 describes Carla "taking the baton from the conductor's stand", implying that she is a conductor.

10. C
Line 8 states that the music festival lasts for "two weeks". Lines 13-14 state that Mateo was practising the piano before the concert, implying that he is a pianist. Line 19 states that Carla spoke in her "native tongue" and that this was "Italian".

11. D
Line 1 states that Mateo was "thrilled", which means 'exhilarated'. Lines 20-21 state that Mateo was "suddenly gripped with apprehension", showing that he was anxious. Lines 25-26 state that Mateo beamed "with delight", showing that he was gleeful.

12. B
"eminent" and 'illustrious' both mean 'famous' or 'well-respected'.

Test 10 — pages 41-44

1. A
"deep" can mean 'very far down'. When the dungeon is described as "deep", this means it is far underground.

2. A
Lines 9-16 describe how the prisoner no longer thinks about the past or future. Instead, he is "lost in a maze of wandering thoughts" (line 17) and sits in a "stupor of despair" (line 20). 'a stupor' means 'a daze'.

3. B
Lines 9-10 state that it is because "he has lived so long enthralled / Alone in dungeon gloom" that the narrator has "lost regret and hope" (line 11).

4. C
'to sigh for something' can mean 'to long for something'. Therefore, when the narrator says the prisoner doesn't sigh for freedom anymore, it means he no longer pines to be released.

5. A
'despondent' means 'dispirited'. The narrator has fallen into a "stupor of despair" (line 20) and "pines not for the light of day" (line 13), suggesting that he has given up on getting out of the dungeon and has lost his will to fight.

6. B
Lines 21-24 state that the prisoner was not always so despairing. Therefore we can infer that the "fitful flickering fire" which was a "strange uncertain light" (line 28) is the prisoner's former lack of despair, and a faint hopefulness that better things may come.

7. D
Lines 31-32 state that strange fancies had "filled his cell with scenes of life / And forms of living men". 'fancies' can mean 'hallucinations', showing that these fancies are products of his imagination.

8. D
"reason" is another word for 'the ability to think logically'. Here the narrator is wondering whether the prisoner's mind will be taken over by irrational hallucinations and whether he will lose his ability to think clearly.

9. C
Line 39 states two men "have entered now his cell". Lines 41-48 then describe what the men said and how they reacted. This implies that the prisoner is not having a dream, as he thinks he might be in line 40, but that the men are really there.

10. D
Line 47 states that the elder man "looked for gleaming ecstasy". "ecstasy" means 'extreme joy', showing that this man expected the prisoner to be incredibly happy.

11. A
"rack" and 'trouble' can both mean 'torment'.

12. B
"flitting" and 'darting' both mean 'moving swiftly'.

1.   C
In line 1, the narrator compares the way the car flew into the air to the way a firework flies upwards. Fireworks fly upward quickly and explosively, so from this we can infer that the car flew upwards suddenly and violently.

2.   B
Lines 3-4 describe how Lilo "could see through the windscreen that the race track was hurtling towards her", showing the car was descending having been thrown upwards. "Moments later" (line 5), she heard the sound of crunching metal and felt the rocking of the car. This implies that it's the impact of the car on the track that causes the noise and rocking motion.

3.   A
Line 9 states that the crash occurred where Lilo was able to see the other cars "heading down the final straight of the penultimate lap". The "final straight" describes the part of the racecourse just before the finishing line. "penultimate" means 'second to last'.

4.   A
Line 13 states that Lilo's pit team were "running to her assistance". Therefore, this suggests that Thunderbolt's "other ideas" do not involve being fixed. Immediately after this, his "engine started to purr stubbornly" (line 14) implying that Thunderbolt wanted to continue driving.

5.   D
'impaired' means 'damaged'. Though Thunderbolt is still able to drive, his chassis is not in "good shape" (line 17) after the crash. This implies that the chassis has been weakened, but has not been fully destroyed.

6.   B
Lines 15-16 state that "Lilo scanned the car's vitals via the onboard computer. Fortunately, none of her companion's internal functions were harmed". This shows that Lilo used the car's computer to determine that its interior was not harmed by the crash.

7.   C
In lines 18-20, Lilo states that she didn't see the rocks in the road which caused her to crash, and that she thinks Aaron planted them there so he could overtake her. This implies that Aaron is another driver who Lilo believes left the rocks in her way in order to overtake her.

8.   D
In line 20, Lilo says to Thunderbolt, "We need to get you to the garage", showing that she cares for Thunderbolt and wants to see him repaired. The fact that she pats the steering wheel to reassure Thunderbolt after saying this shows that she is affectionate towards Thunderbolt.

9.   C
The term "old friend" is used to describe a loyal companion or a person that someone has been friends with for a long time.

10.   A
Lines 25-26 describe how Lilo and Thunderbolt drove off after the crash. We can infer the pit team are confused by this as they had gone to offer Lilo and Thunderbolt assistance (lines 12-13), so are confused as to why they have driven away.

11.   B
"subsided" and 'abated' can both mean 'became less intense'.

12.   A
"discernible" and 'distinguishable' both mean 'able to be seen'.

Choral Chaos

1.   **Ian**
2.   **Linda**
3.   **Milo**
4.   **Leo**
5.   **Ruth**
6.   **Alfred**
7.   **Ryan**
8.   **Peggy**
9.   **Paul**
10.   **Adrian**
11.   **Julie**
12.   **Nico**

1.   C
'innumerable' can mean 'countless' or 'very many'. Lines 2-3 state that "our galaxy alone may contain trillions" of exoplanets, suggesting that there are a great number of them.

2.   A
Line 5 states that, during the nineteenth century, "scientists were unconvinced" that exoplanets existed. 'sceptical' and "unconvinced" both mean 'dubious'.

3.   C
Lines 7-8 state that, after the discovery of 51 Pegasis b using the "wobble method", "an international search for exoplanets began".

4.   B
Lines 8-10 state that Butler and Marcy discovered exoplanets after reassessing data they already had. They did this during the "search" (line 8) that had been sparked by the discovery of 51 Pegasis b. This announcement occurred in 1995 (line 5). Therefore, Butler and Marcy must have already had data showing signs of exoplanets in 1995.

5.   A
"state-of-the-art" means 'using the newest ideas or features'. Therefore we can infer that when the CoRoT satellite was built, it was built using the latest techniques and technology.

6.   B
'in commission' and 'in service' can both mean 'to be in use'.

7.   B
Lines 19-21 state that scientists are looking for terrestrial exoplanets in habitable zones that "could hold water, a prerequisite for life on Earth". Line 27 implies that scientists are doing this as part of the search for "extraterrestrial life".

8.   B
Line 16 states the CoRoT satellite "functioned from 2006 to 2012", so it was no longer in use in 2016.

9.   C
Lines 20-21 state that exoplanets in habitable zones "could hold water". Line 25 states that Proxima Centauri b is "in a habitable zone", therefore it is possible there could be water on the surface of the planet.

10.   D
Lines 23-24 state that " In 2016, the closest terrestrial exoplanet yet, Proxima Centauri b, was confirmed by data", but the distance between this planet and Earth is not mentioned.

11.   A
"characteristics" and 'properties' both mean 'attributes'.

12.   C
"intensified" and 'escalated' both mean 'become more intense'.

Test 13 — pages 54-57

1. C
Lines 4-12 describe the appearance of Othere. Line 6 states he was "tall and stately", implying he was imposing and dignified.

2. A
Line 13 states that Othere had "a kind of laugh in his speech". This implies that his speech was cheerful. 'affable' means 'pleasant or good-natured'.

3. C
Line 3 states that Alfred was known as "the Lover of Truth", showing he values knowledge. Lines 18-20 state that Alfred "wrote down the wondrous tale / Of him who was first to sail / Into the Arctic Seas." Therefore we can infer Alfred wanted to write a factual account of Othere's voyage.

4. B
In line 23, Othere states that "To the east" of his home "are wild mountain-chains". Line 25 states that "To the westward all is sea." This implies he lives both near mountains and the sea.

5. D
Line 27 states that, while living on the land, Othere's "heart was ill at ease", implying he felt restless. Lines 33-34 state that Othere "could not eat nor sleep" for thinking about the seas and "undiscovered deep", showing he wished to explore uncharted waters. Lines 36-37 state "To the northward stretched the desert, / How fair I fain would know". Here, "desert" refers to the sea, showing Othere wishes to know how far the sea stretches to the north. There is no mention of him wanting to see whether the seas matched the descriptions by other mariners.

6. A
Line 26 states that, before sailing to the North Cape, Othere "ploughed the land with horses", implying that he was a farmer.

7. B
Lines 39-40 state that Othere sailed "due north, / As far as the whale-ships go", showing the whale-ships must sail north of Helgoland, where Othere is from (line 2).

8. C
Lines 41-42 state that "The days grew longer and longer, / Till they became as one". This means eventually, one day seemed to merge into another as there was no night, implying the sun stopped setting.

9. D
Line 48 states that the North Cape is "huge and haggard", implying it is both towering and weather-beaten ("haggard" means 'worn'). Line 49 states that the North Cape is "unknown", suggesting it is also unexplored.

10. D
Line 2 states that Othere is from "Helgoland". In line 16, Alfred is referred to as "King of the Saxons". Lines 19-20 state that Othere is the "first to sail / Into the Arctic seas", suggesting that the North Cape is in those waters. There is no mention of the type of boat Othere sailed on.

11. B
"hearty and hale" and 'strong and healthy' mean 'fit and well'.

12. A
"sagas" and 'tales' both mean 'stories'.

Test 14 — pages 58-61

1. C
Lines 1-2 states that the "houses above a certain rent" (i.e. the houses with the highest rents) are rented by women. Since the richer members of Cranford are more likely to rent the most expensive houses, the richer people of Cranford must be women.

2. D
Lines 2-5 state that a man may be absent from Cranford because he is "with his regiment, his ship or closely engaged in business in the great neighbouring town of Drumble".

3. C
Lines 5-6 state that the "great neighbouring town of Drumble" is "distant only twenty miles on a railroad", showing that there is a settlement twenty miles away from Cranford.

4. A
Lines 7-8 state that Cranford ladies have "an occasional little quarrel, spirited out in a few peppery words", showing that their disagreements are few and short-lived.

5. B
"tenor" can mean 'the general direction of something', especially of a life, while "even" can mean 'smooth'. Therefore, "even tenor" suggests that the course of the Cranford ladies' lives is settled.

6. B
Lines 9-11 state that "Their dress is very independent of fashion; as they observe, "What does it signify how we dress here at Cranford, where everybody knows us?" And if they go from home, "What does it signify how we dress here, where nobody knows us?"" Therefore they dress uniquely, not allowing their company to affect how they dress.

7. C
'to be at liberty' can mean 'to be free'. Line 16 states that the narrator should "be at liberty" to take calls, meaning she needs to be free of responsibilities after twelve.

8. A
Line 16 states that the calling hours are "from twelve to three". Lines 18-19 state that the Cranford ladies are "never to let more than three days elapse between receiving a call and returning it" and are "never to stay longer than a quarter of an hour". Therefore, it would be unacceptable to return a call after three o'clock, more than three days after the initial call.

9. D
Lines 23-24 state that, to judge how long a call is taking, you should "keep thinking about the time" and "not allow yourself to forget it in conversation", suggesting that people think more about the time than their conversations in Cranford.

10. D
Lines 25-26 state that, because everyone is trying to keep track of the time that has passed, "no absorbing subject was even spoken about", suggesting that Cranford's rules about calls limits what can be discussed.

11. C
"regulations" and 'guidelines' can both mean 'rules'.

12. A
"absorbing" and 'captivating' can both mean 'very interesting'.

Puzzles 5 — page 62

Target Practice
Starting with 'energetic' and moving clockwise, the correct words are: **ACTIVE, INTACT, BITTER, SEVERE, ABSURD, LETHAL, SUDDEN.** The word in the middle is: **TENDERLY**

Cunning Combinations

The words are: **RETAILED, STRAINING, PASTURE, HESITATE, TRAIPSING, SIMPLY.**

Test 15 — pages 63-66

1. C
Lines 4-5 state that "As the light of the dawn stirred the inhabitants of the rural scene, so the blinding rays woke Tim", showing it was the bright sunrise that woke Tim.

2. B
If something is said 'to command a view', it means it gives a particularly good view over something else. Therefore, since the hill "commanded a fine view over the surrounding landscape" (line 7), it means it allowed Tim to see the surrounding area well from his position at the top.

3. C
Lines 8-10 state that Tim could see "uncultivated heath, meadows peppered with sheep, expansive corn fields and lush meadows that were slowly browning, ready for the hay harvest". There is no mention of fields containing hay bales.

4. B
"gridlock" (line 13) means 'traffic jam', therefore the "steady drone" describes the sound of traffic on the roads.

5. C
Line 13 mentions Tim's "tower block", which is a tall building containing flats. These are usually found in urban areas, so this implies that Tim lives in a city.

6. D
Lines 14-15 state that "Tim tried to conjure up details of the previous evening... but the memories slipped through his head like water". This implies that Tim found it difficult to recall the memories, as they were flowing out of his head quickly.

7. A
Someone is incredibly surprised if it's said that their "mouth fell open". In line 20, the creature states that "It's rude to stare!". This suggests Tim is shocked at the creature's appearance, and this is why he stares and his mouth falls open.

8. B
In line 22, Tim asks the animal "How are you talking? You're not meant to be able to talk!", showing that it is the fact that the creature can speak that most surprises Tim.

9. C
Line 25 states the creature had a "cotton tail". This is characteristic of a rabbit.

10. B
In lines 23-24, the creature states "I suppose you won't want me to tell you where you are", before jumping away. This implies that it can help Tim, who is unsure where he is. Directly after this, Tim chases after the creature, showing it's because he thinks the creature can tell him where he is that he follows it.

11. A
"indignantly" and 'bitterly' can both mean 'angrily'.

12. B
"vigorously" and 'energetically' can both mean 'to put a lot of effort into something'.

Test 16 — pages 67-70

1. C
Lines 1-2 state that the Terracotta Army was buried "to the north-east of the city of Xi'an, in the Shaanxi Province of China".

2. D
Lines 1-3 state that farmers "unearthed pieces of a pottery figure" when they "set out to build a well", showing it was people digging for water that found the first traces of the Army.

3. B
Lines 6-7 state that the Terracotta Army "was built to guard and serve the great Chinese king and emperor, Qin Shi Huang, in the afterlife", showing it was responsible for protecting him in the next life.

4. C
Lines 9-10 state that the figures that have been found include "foot soldiers, standing archers and chariots, complete with their drivers and horses". There is no mention of mounted archers, who are archers on horseback.

5. C
Line 13 states that each figure is "unique", so they cannot be 'generic' (which means 'not individually made').

6. A
Lines 13-15 state that there "would have been even greater variations between the figures than there are now, as each figure was initially hand-painted with bright colours". This implies the figures no longer have paint on them.

7. D
Lines 19-20 state that the building of the mausoleum started "when the king assumed the throne at the age of 13". When someone 'assumes the throne', it means that their reign begins.

8. B
Lines 20-21 state that although the tomb was "seemingly unfinished", it was "sealed after the king's death". This shows it was not completed during his lifetime.

9. D
Lines 23-24 state that Qin Shi Huang may have believed mercury was the "elixir of life". It is therefore likely that mercury was included in the tomb as it was believed to have life-giving powers.

10. C
Lines 25-27 state that there are people who are opposed to beginning excavation work on the main tomb because the "technology does not currently exist to unearth the treasures without damaging them". This implies that, once technology has developed, excavations on the tomb will begin.

11. A
"excavated" and 'uncovered' can both mean 'unearthed'.

12. B
"Miraculously" and 'remarkably' can both mean 'amazingly'.

Test 17 — pages 71-74

1. B
Lines 1-2 state that when Oak smiled, "the corners of his mouth spread till they were within an unimportant distance of his ears". Here, "unimportant" means 'small', showing that his smile spread almost as far as his ears. Lines 2-3 state that when Oak smiled, "his eyes were reduced to chinks, and diverging wrinkles appeared round them", showing that his eyes narrowed and wrinkles appeared around them. There is no mention of dimples in his cheeks.

2. D
Line 5 states that Oak's "Christian name was Gabriel". "Christian name" means 'first name', which implies Oak is his surname, making his full name Gabriel Oak.

3. C
Line 10 says that Oak "went to church, but yawned privately", which shows that he goes to church, but doesn't have any enthusiasm for it. Therefore, Oak has a half-hearted attitude to religion.

9

4.   A

That Oak "thought of what there would be for dinner when he meant to be listening to the sermon" shows that he did not concentrate on sermons. This means that his mind wandered during them.

5.   B

Line 7 states that Oak was "hampered by his best clothes". "hampered" means 'restricted', implying that Oak did not feel at ease in his best clothes.

6.   B

Lines 13-14 state that when Oak's acquaintances were "in tantrums, he was considered rather a bad man; when they were pleased, he was rather a good man", showing that their opinion of Oak was fickle (which means 'changeable').

7.   A

That people sometimes saw Oak's character as "a kind of pepper-and-salt mixture" implies that they thought Oak's morals were mixed. This means they thought that there were good and bad aspects of his character.

8.   C

Lines 16-17 state that Oak lived "six times as many working-days as Sundays", so that his "appearance in his old clothes was most peculiarly his own". This implies Oak wears his working clothes six times a week (every day except Sunday) and therefore only wears his best clothes on Sundays.

9.   B

Lines 16-17 state that on working-days, Oak wears his "old clothes". Line 18 states that Oak wore a "felt hat", which is a cloth hat. Lines 19-20 state that he wore "a coat like Dr. Johnson's", which shows that he wasn't wearing Dr. Johnson's coat, just one like it. Line 20 states that he also wore "ordinary" leather leggings, which suggests they are not distinctive.

10.   D

Line 21 states the boots were "emphatically large" and "roomy", showing they were spacious. Lines 21-22 state that "any wearer might stand in a river all day long and know nothing of damp", showing they were also 'robust'.

11.   A

"countenance" and 'appearance' both mean 'demeanour'.

12.   B

"postponing" and 'delaying' both mean 'putting off'.

Puzzles 6 — page 75

Puzzle Paws

B	U	L	L
N	E	W	T
S	E	A	L
D	E	E	R

M	A	C	A	W
K	O	A	L	A
S	L	O	T	H
H	O	R	S	E
W	H	A	L	E

B	A	B	O	O	N
D	O	N	K	E	Y
R	A	B	B	I	T
T	O	U	C	A	N
C	O	U	G	A	R
H	O	R	N	E	T

Test 18 — pages 76-79

1.   D

Line 8 states that the Tharsis Region is full of "arid deserts", so the weather must be dry. Lines 8-9 state that there were occasional gusts and storms that required the team to "take cover", so the weather is sometimes very windy.

2.   C

Line 1 states that Ahmed has been on Mars for 231 sols. Line 17 states that there are 669 sols in a Mars year, so there are (669 – 231) 438 more sols before Ahmed has spent an entire Mars year on the planet.

3.   A

Line 7 states that volcanoes in the Tharsis region are "extinct". Line 10 states that Ascraeus Mons is in the Tharsis region. This means that Ascraeus Mons is extinct, not active.

4.   A

Line 12 states that the team travelled to the Tharsis region for "important work". Lines 13-14 state that members of the team analysed atmospheric samples taken from the Tharsis region. This suggests that the purpose of the mission was to collect atmospheric samples.

5.   C

Line 25 states Ahmed wakes up at 7:00 when he is at the base. Line 2 states that he waited for four hours before leaving the base, so he left the base at 11:00. Lines 14-15 state that he attended to the robots for an hour before returning to the base, so he returned to the base at 12:00.

6.   B

Lines 19-20 state that Ahmed is writing in the Earth year 2073. Line 16 states that Ahmed's son turns eight "tomorrow", meaning he was born eight Earth years ago. Therefore, Ahmed's son was born in 2065.

7.   B

Line 16 states that Ahmed's son's birthday is tomorrow. Lines 19-20 state that it is two weeks from when Ahmed is writing until the end of the Earth year. This means that Ahmed's son was born in December, not January.

8.   C

Line 6 states that the Tharsis region is located to the "north" of Ahmed's base. Lines 6-7 state that the Tharsis region is on the planet's equator. Therefore, Ahmed's base must be located in the southern hemisphere. Line 25 states that the team have a "routine" of going to bed at 21:00.

9.   B

Lines 16-17 state that Ahmed found it "difficult" to keep track of Earth days. Line 18 states that it took a long time for Ahmed to get used to Mars time.

10.   A

Line 6 states that "Yestersol" the team returned from "the Tharsis region". Lines 22-23 state that at some point the team "will go back to" the region they "returned from yestersol" to investigate Olympus Mons. Therefore, Olympus Mons must be in the Tharsis region.

11.   D

Line 6 states that the team returned from the Tharsis region "Yestersol" but not how long the mission took.

12.   B

Line 25 states that Ahmed finds the routine at the base "monotonous". This suggests he dislikes the predictability of his days at the base.

Test 19 — pages 80-83

1. C
Lines 1-3 state that the teenagers were walking Ravidat's dog when they found the cave.

2. B
Lines 19-20 state the cave is named Lascaux. Line 3 states the cave was located near the village of Montignac.

3. D
Lines 17-18 state that the paintings provide archaeologists with an insight into "prehistoric lifestyles and beliefs".

4. B
"Felines" means 'cats'. Line 15 states that the chamber's paintings include images of large cats. This suggests that the chamber must be named after the paintings on its walls.

5. D
Lines 21-22 state that two of the teenagers who found the paintings became tour guides, but they don't state the number of tour guides in total.

6. A
'extensive' means 'large'. Lines 9-10 state that there "are over 600 paintings and 1500 engravings in total which are spread across several chambers", showing the number of paintings and engravings is large.

7. D
Line 7 states that the boys told their teacher.
Line 7 also states that the teacher was a member of the local prehistory society, so he likely realised the importance of the paintings and shared this information with others.

8. A
Line 21 states that the paintings "captivated... their discoverers", so they likely became tour guides at the cave due to their interest in the cave paintings.

9. B
Line 24 states that "visitors' breath" helped cause the paint to fade. Line 25 states that tourists can visit the replica paintings "instead", so tourists can still enjoy the paintings without damaging the originals.

10. C
Lines 19-20 state that the number of visitors grew after the discovery. Line 24 suggests that "visitors' breath" helped cause the paint to deteriorate, showing that it was a consequence of the discovery that the paintings have been damaged.

11. D
"belies" and 'conceals' can both mean 'disguises'.

12. A
"depicted" and 'portrayed' both mean 'represent'.

Test 20 — pages 84-87

1. C
'oppressed' can mean 'troubled'. The lion is described as "heat oppress'd" because he is troubled by how hot it is, i.e. he is very warm.

2. D
Line 6 states that the mouse mistakes the lion for "something else", showing she wasn't aware she was walking over a lion.

3. A
Line 11 states that the lion awoke with "wrath immense", showing he was grumpy or bad-tempered. Line 4 describes the lion as having a "royal back" and line 10 describes the lion as a "monarch", which means 'king'.

4. B
Lines 9-10 suggest that you should "tremble when you hear" that the mouse enters the lion's ear. This suggests the narrator expects the reader to be frightened of the prospect of the mouse exploring the lion's ear, showing the lion is terrifying.

5. B
Line 27 states that "With dreadful rage he stamp'd and tore". "rage" is another word for "fury".

6. D
Line 33 states that the mouse applies "patient labour" to the situation which suggests she is taking time over her work to ensure it is completed well.

7. C
Line 23 states that it was "nearly twelve months" after the lion and the mouse's first meeting that the lion became trapped in the net, so it wasn't quite one year.

8. B
Lines 11-12 state that the lion "woke with wrath immense / And shook his head to cast her thence". This suggests the lion is tormented by the mouse's actions in the first part of the poem. Line 36 states, "A lion, by a mouse set free", which shows the mouse becomes the lion's saviour, as she set him free from the net.

9. D
Line 36 states that the mouse set the lion free but not how the lion reacted.

10. A
The lion shows the mouse mercy when he "thought it best at least to give / His little pris'ner a reprieve" (lines 21-22). The mouse then saves the lion from the net, showing the lion's kindness was not wasted.

11. B
"implored" means 'entreated'.

12. D
"reprieve" means 'pardon'.

Puzzles 7 — page 88

The Case of the Broken Vase

The person who knocked the vase over was: Alan.

Test 21 — pages 89-92

1. D
Lines 1-2 state that the "Thai Elephant Conservation Centre is dedicated to the care and rehabilitation of the country's elephants". Lines 2-3 state that the centre "focuses on supporting some of the country's captive elephants" showing its primary aim is to look after and rehabilitate captive elephants.

2. C
Lines 2-3 state that the "centre focuses on supporting some of the country's captive elephants (of which there are about 2700)", showing there are about 2700 elephants in captivity in Thailand, the country where the Thai Elephant Conservation Centre is located.

3. A
Lines 7-8 state that Richard Lair runs the centre and is "affectionately known" as "Professor Elephant". "Professor" is a title given to someone very knowledgeable, so you can infer that "Professor Elephant" is a nickname that has stemmed from his work with and knowledge of elephants.

4. B

Lines 7-9 describe how Richard Lair and Dave Soldier thought up a plan to help the "residents at the conservation centre". Since the conservation centre works to care for elephants (lines 1-2), the "residents" must be the centre's elephants.

5. C

Line 10 states that elephant handlers are called mahouts.

6. B

Lines 11-13 state that Lair and Soldier came up with an idea to "benefit the elephants" and "create an additional source of income for the centre". This idea was the Thai Elephant Orchestra.

7. C

Lines 13-15 state that Dave Soldier was "interested in exploring the musical capabilities of elephants", showing that Soldier wanted to explore how elephants responded to music.

8. A

Lines 17-18 state that the instruments were "designed to be indestructible". "indestructible" means 'unbreakable'. This implies the instruments were made so the elephants couldn't break them as they might normal instruments.

9. C

Lines 21-22 state that the Lanna scale "is traditional in northern Thai music and is therefore familiar to the elephants".

10. D

Lines 23-24 state that the elephants' music is made up of "deep, reverberating sounds". 'resonant' means 'a deep, resounding noise', so describes the elephants' music.

11. A

"collaborated" and 'co-operated' both mean 'worked together'.

12. B

"prowess" and 'talent' both mean 'skill'.

Test 22 — pages 93-96

1. A

Line 1 states that the sergeant told the cadets to line up in "height order". Since Diggory is at the front of the line, he must therefore be the tallest.

2. C

Line 24 states that it is "2 o'clock". Line 4 states that it was 20 minutes since lunch and that the lunch break lasted for 30 minutes. This means the lunch break finished at 1:40 pm and started 30 minutes before that (at 1:10 pm).

3. B

Lines 6-10 describe how, "as a line slowly appeared", Gemma, Dean and Ana started to take their places in it. This means they were waiting for some of the line to form before attempting to find their place within it.

4. C

Line 8 states that "Gemma lined up behind Cathy", showing Gemma is shorter than Cathy. Lines 8-9 state that Ana is taller than Cathy, so Ana must also be taller than Gemma.

5. A

Line 15 states that "Gemma's heart sank". Immediately after this, the Mud Trail is described. From this we can infer that Gemma is discouraged by the prospect of the Mud Trail.

6. D

Line 24 states that it's "2 o'clock" when the cadets start the Mud Trail. Line 20 states that the sergeant says he would be surprised if any of the cadets finish the Mud Trail in under 4 hours, meaning he expects most of them to finish over 4 hours after 2:00 pm (i.e. after 6:00 pm).

7. D

Line 17 states that the Mud Trail ran "around the army base, into Frinwick woods". Line 23 states that the finishing line for the Mud Trail was on the beach.

8. B

Line 10 states that, before the Mud Trail, the recruits were carrying a 5-kilogram bag. Lines 13-14 state that the recruits must pick up either 1 or 2 extra kilograms, meaning they must carry either 6 or 7 kilograms while completing the Mud Trail.

9. B

Lines 22-23 state that there is a "2-kilometre run back inland...to the base".

10. D

Line 3 states that there was a "20-kilometre run" in the morning. Line 16 states that the Mud Trail is 15 kilometres. Lines 22-23 state that there is a "2-kilometre run" from the end of the Mud Trail back to the base. Therefore, Gemma will have run (20 + 15 + 2) 37 kilometres by the end of the day.

11. A

"harshly" means 'in a severe manner'. Line 1 states that the sergeant "shouted" orders at the cadets, while "glaring" at them. Line 12 states that the sergeant calls the cadets a "bunch of no-goods". This shows the sergeant treats the cadets harshly.

12. C

The record time for the Mud Trail is given (in line 19), but the record time for the 20-kilometre run is not mentioned.

Test 23 — pages 97-100

1. B

Line 4 states that the floor in the card-room was "disgracefully dusty", showing that it had not been cleaned recently.

2. B

Lines 4-5 state that "suddenly the lights went out... Liddy was stunned with fright", showing Liddy was initially startled when the lights went out.

3. D

Line 9 states that the figure "darted across the veranda and out of sight" when the narrator looked at it. This implies that it did not want to be seen.

4. A

"petrified" means 'unable to move out of fear' and "amazement" describes a state of surprise or shock. Therefore, the narrator was so scared and shocked that they were unable to move.

5. B

Lines 14-15 state that, after asking Liddy to come with her, the narrator was going to leave Liddy and go and find the door alone. Line 16 states Liddy "moved at that", implying Liddy didn't like the prospect of being left by herself.

6. C

Line 1 states that the characters are originally in the card-room. Lines 16-17 state that they move from this room "to the billiard-room", showing the two rooms must be connected.

7. C

"ghostly" can mean 'eerie', showing the narrator was spooked by the evening's events. There is no information in the text to support the idea that the narrator thinks the house is haunted or that they have seen a ghost.

8. D

From the fact that Liddy and the narrator were alarmed by what happened, it can be inferred that they left the lights on to help make them feel safer.

9.　C

From the fact that Liddy is frightened throughout the passage, we can infer that Liddy was too scared to go to bed.

10.　A

'distraught' means 'distressed'. Line 5 states Liddy is "stunned with fright" when the lights go out. Line 10 states Liddy collapses after seeing the figure in the window. Line 14 states that Liddy "groaned" at the prospect of going any further. This shows that Liddy is distraught during the passage.

11.　B

"groaned" and 'whimpered' both mean 'moaned'.

12.　C

"surveillance" and 'scrutiny' both mean 'observation'.

Puzzles 8 — page 101

Riddle Round-Up

Daisy is in the **bank**. Marigold is in the **hotel**. Snowdrop is in the **stable**.

Test 24 — pages 102-105

1.　B

Magpies are known for collecting different objects and line 7 states that Patrick thinks the attic is an "intriguing treasure trove". This shows the attic is full of interesting items.

2.　D

Lines 3-4 state that Patrick's "excitement... was overwhelming". Line 5 states that he swings his torch around "with wild abandon". This suggests his reaction is uncontrollable exuberance.

3.　C

Line 3 states that the attic is a "forbidden room". It is likely, that Patrick does not want his family to know he is in there.

4.　D

Lines 8-9 state that the attic features "an old rocking chair" and "a pile of what might be paperback novels or worn diaries". Line 11 states that there are "old toys". There is no mention of photographs in the attic.

5.　C

'belonging to another century' means the clothes are so old that they look out of place compared to modern clothes.

6.　B

Line 3 states that Patrick walks into the "darkness" of the attic, which means that it is dim inside. Line 11 states that the attic has "old toys and ornaments strewn across the floor", showing it is untidy.

7.　A

Line 19 states that Patrick "wanted to examine these exquisite figures more closely".

8.　D

Line 21 states that Patrick has "no free hands" with which to carry the torch, meaning he must be carrying the chessboard with both hands.

9.　B

Line 23 states that Patrick had "left the attic door open". It is likely that the person calling out had seen the door and wondered why it was open.

10.　B

Line 23 states that Patrick has "absent-mindedly" left the door open. Line 24 states that leaving the door open "would allow his family to find him easily". This means Patrick is worried that he is going to be caught as a result of his carelessness.

11.　C

"commotion" and 'racket' both mean 'noise'.

12.　A

"resplendent" and 'magnificent' both mean 'impressive'.

Test 25 — pages 106-109

1.　C

'Environment' in the name "World Environment Day" (line 1) relates to the natural world, meaning planting trees is a suitable activity for World Environment Day.

2.　B

Line 6 states that Maathai was born in "rural Kenya".

3.　A

Lines 10-11 state that "chopping down trees" was causing the soil to dry out. This in turn caused crops to fail.

4.　D

Lines 11-12 state that "planting trees was the simplest solution" to the problems Kenyans were facing with crop growth. Therefore, the Green Belt Movement was an organisation focused on putting this solution into practice.

5.　C

Line 15 states that the saplings were "free", so there was no financial risk in taking the saplings.

6.　B

Lines 16-17 state that Maathai's group paid planters money for "every tree they planted and cared for".

7.　A

"efforts" means 'attempts'. "combat" can mean 'reduce or prevent'.

8.　D

Line 13 states that Maathai started the Green Belt Movement in 1977. Line 25 states that Maathai won the Nobel Peace Prize in 2004. The time between those two events is greater than 25 years.

9.　A

Line 12 states that planting trees would "maintain nutrients in the soil". Lines 21-22 state that Kenyan women who worked with the Green Belt Movement went on to combat poverty and other problems.

10.　C

Lines 9-11 state that Maathai noticed that her fellow Kenyans were having problems related to growing food, showing she was compassionate. Line 12 states that Maathai came up with a "solution" to the problem, showing she was resourceful.

11.　C

"accumulate" and 'amass' both mean 'collect'.

12.　B

"prestigious" and 'acclaimed' both mean 'respected'.

Test 26 — pages 110-113

1.　B

Lines 2-3 state that the narrator "was determined to be the first" to the top of the mountain.

2.　D

Lines 4-5 state that Rio is the narrator's home. This is likely to affect their opinion since they will think fondly of their home.

3.　A

"vitality" means 'liveliness'. The narrator is therefore commenting on how lively the city is.

4. B

"prelude" means 'something that comes just before something else'. Later in the passage, the "monster's head rose out of the water", which suggests that the ripples are a sign that the creature is nearing the surface.

5. A

"anxious" can mean 'eager for something to happen'. Lines 18-19 state that the narrator is waiting in "nervous anticipation" for the creature to appear.

6. C

Line 20 states that the water "spurted" out of the ocean. This would make the water look like it is erupting from the ocean, like lava from a volcano.

7. D

Line 20 states that the creature's head is "Scaly", not smooth.

8. B

"unwaveringly" means 'without stopping or faltering'. This means the creature did not stop walking.

9. C

Lines 24-25 state that the narrator is amazed by "the way this juggernaut shifted the whole ocean before it". A "juggernaut" means a 'strong and powerful force', which suggests the narrator is amazed by the creature's strength and power.

10. B

Lines 26-27 state that the narrator is worried that the creature will not return to the sea.

11. A

"prolong" and 'lengthen' can both mean 'to make something last a longer time'.

12. C

"inconceivable" and 'incredible' both mean 'unbelievable'.

Puzzles 9 — page 114

Bookshelf Sequence

The correct position of each book is as follows:
HISTORY: 1800-1900 — 4
DICTIONARY — 5
THE TREASURE MAP by Mallory Schiff — 7
ENCYCLOPEDIA — 9
HISTORY: 1600-1700 — 3
THE MYSTERY by John Quest — 6
THE HAUNTED HOUSE by Timothy Spook — 8
HISTORY: 1400-1500 — 2
THESAURUS — 1

Test 27 — pages 115-118

1. D

Lines 1-2 state that Eric thought he heard his brother say "you are a thief!" but "it was conscience who had borrowed the voice", showing that it was Eric's conscience that prompted him to return the coins. This implies that he was beginning to feel guilty for stealing.

2. A

To be "plunged in books" means to be 'engrossed in reading'. The word 'pretended' implies that Eric was not really reading but only acting as though he was.

3. B

A "sickly smile" refers to a smile that is false or exaggerated. Since Eric gave Duncan a "sickly smile", we can assume Eric was not genuinely happy.

4. C

Lines 6-7 describe how Eric walked from the place where the money box was kept back to his own study, reaching his desk only just before Duncan and Montagu appeared on the landing. We can therefore infer that the footsteps Montagu heard were Eric's, since there was no-one else in the studies (line 12).

5. B

Line 10 states that Duncan noted that Eric was "grinding as usual". "grinding" means 'working', so this shows Duncan is used to seeing Eric studying hard.

6. C

'deserted' means 'unoccupied'. In line 12, Montagu observes that Eric is "the only fellow in the studies", showing that, except for Eric, the studies are deserted.

7. B

Lines 5-6 state that Eric "had no time to take out the key and put it back where he found it", showing that he must not have left the box quite as he found it. In line 19, he worries that Duncan and Montagu might "discover the key in the box".

8. A

If someone is described as 'having a burning brow', it can mean they are troubled. Lines 16-20 describe Eric's regret and feeling of guilt about attempting to steal the money. Since his "burning brow" is described directly after this, we can assume that it has been brought about by worrying.

9. A

"guilty" can mean 'responsible for wrongdoing'. Since the pockets were where Eric first placed the coins when he attempted to steal them (line 3), we can infer this is why the pocket is described as "guilty".

10. D

Line 24 states that, after finding the coin, Eric thought "he was a thief, even actually". Since Eric attempted to return the money, we can infer he wanted to get rid of this last coin so as to no longer seem like a thief.

11. B

"good-humouredly" and 'cheerfully' both mean 'merrily'.

12. D

"accursed" and 'detestable' both mean 'hateful'.

Test 28 — pages 119-122

1. D

Lines 6-7 state that "the paths were created as a way for coastguards to patrol the cliffs so they could watch out for smugglers on the lower beaches". This implies that the coastal paths were built to enable coastguards to look over beaches.

2. A

Line 10 states that the SWCP starts "in Minehead". Line 1 states that the coastal path runs "from north Somerset", so Minehead must be in north Somerset.

3. B

Line 11 states that "Almost half of the 630-mile trail is in Cornwall". Line 3 states that the trail is "over 1000 km long". Therefore, around 500 km (half of the length of the entire coastal path) must be in Cornwall.

4. C

Lines 13-14 state that the SWCP passes through Cornwall from Marsland Mouth to "the Tamar Estuary near the Cornish border in the south east". Line 15 states that the route "then moves into Devon", so the Tamar Estuary must be on the border between Devon and Cornwall.

5. B

Lines 3-5 state that walking the SWCP requires a lot of climbing, but not which section has the longest ascent.

6. C

Line 21 states the route "attracts walkers of all abilities." This means that use of the path is not exclusive to any one group.

7. D

Line 1 states that the SWCP starts in "north Somerset". Line 10 states that the South West Coast Path starts "in Minehead, on the boundaries of the Exmoor National Park". So Exmoor National Park, and therefore the Exmoor Coastal Heaths, must be in Somerset and not Cornwall.

8. B

Line 18 states that Tintagel is "King Arthur's legendary castle". There is no mention of his burial place being here.

9. D

Lines 21-22 state that the SWCP takes walkers "an average of around 8 weeks to complete". Since there are 7 days in a week, the path takes (7 × 8) 56 days to complete.

10. C

Lines 6-7 state that, "Historically, the paths were created as a way for coastguards to patrol the cliffs so they could watch out for smugglers". The use of the word 'historically' implies that this is no longer the case, and smugglers are no longer found on the South West Coast Path.

11. B

Lines 25-26 state that it costs "£1000 per mile of path per year" to maintain the path. Line 11 states that the coastal path is 630 miles long, therefore you would expect it to cost (630 × 1000) £630,000 to maintain the paths.

12. A

Lines 24-25 state that the South West Coast Path Association (SWCPA) is a charity. Lines 25-26 imply that the SWCPA assists with the maintenance costs of the path.

Test 29 — pages 123-126

1. C

If something is said to 'occupy a space between fiction and fact', it means that a lot of what we know about it is informed by both factual accounts and stories that cannot be proved. Therefore, not all accounts about the Library of Alexandria are true.

2. A

Line 6 describes Ptolemy I Soter as "a Macedonian general". 'General' is a high-ranking position in the army, showing he was a high-ranking officer.

3. B

A "hub" describes somewhere that is a centre of activity. "scholarship" means 'learning', so the Library of Alexandria was a centre for learning.

4. A

Lines 12-15 describe the features of the Library of Alexandria. Since the complex consisted of "meeting and reading rooms" and "lecture halls", alongside a "monumental number of documents", we can infer it was a place for collecting, creating and sharing information.

5. D

Line 18 states that the scrolls were "stored methodically". 'methodical' means 'well organised', whereas 'unsystematic' means 'disorganised'. Therefore, the Library could not be described as 'unsystematic'.

6. B

Lines 9-10 state that "Egypt fell under control of the Romans in around 30 B.C." Line 21 states that Caesar occupied Alexandria "around 20 years before Egypt fell to Rome", which means that he must have occupied the city in approximately 50 B.C.

7. D

Lines 20-22 state that it was during "Julius Caesar's siege of the city" that "an uncontrollable fire destroyed the Library", implying that the Library was destroyed as a result of the siege.

8. B

Line 20 states that one theory about the destruction of the library is "contested" and that "other people believe" another explanation is more likely. This shows there is more than one view about the Library's history, meaning that its history is disputed.

9. A

If something is described as a "lost treasure", it means it is something of great value that has been lost or destroyed. The Library of Alexandria would be of great historical value if it still stood today.

10. B

Lines 24-26 state that the "Bibliotheca Alexandrina was built to both commemorate the great library, as well as revive the area, so it could once more become a centre of learning".

11. B

"monumental" and 'immense' both mean 'huge'.

12. A

"revive" and 'reinvigorate' both mean 'to bring life back to something'.

Puzzles 10 — page 127

Honeycomb Words

1. GAMBLES
2. RAINBOW
3. FORMULA
4. GRANDER
5. DIAGRAM

Secret Word: SWARM

1. OPINION
2. SILENCE
3. TRAFFIC
4. DISTANT
5. DILEMMA
6. STAGGER

Secret Word: NECTAR

Test 30 — pages 128-131

1. C

In line 1, Winona states: "We've done our best", showing she thinks they've tried their hardest to prepare for the exam.

2. B

In lines 3-4, Winona states "Aunt Harriet says we're not to get up at five to-morrow. We shall have quite a hard enough day as it is". Therefore Aunt Harriet wants Winona and Garnet to get sufficient sleep because they have a tiring day ahead of them.

3. A

In lines 6-7, Garnet states "I feel I've taken in the utmost my brains can hold. There's no room for anything more". This means Garnet thinks she cannot learn anything else that evening.

4. C

If the air is described as 'close', it means it is oppressive. This describes weather that is humid.

5. B

Lines 8-9 state that, as the storm was building up, Winona was "leaning out of the widely opened window, to gaze at the lurid sky". This implies she is interested in the storm and wants to experience it closely. This shows she is captivated by it.

6. B

Lines 13-14 state that "a louder peal resounded. The storm was drawing nearer". The 'peal' is referring to the sound of the thunder. The fact that the thunder was getting louder is evidence that the storm was getting closer.

7. A

"electricity in the air" means the storm and 'temperament' means a person's nature. Therefore, the phrase means that storms have a more powerful effect on some people than others. As this phrase is in a paragraph describing how Garnett is "terribly afraid" of thunder, we can infer that this 'powerful effect' is feeling upset.

8. D

The phrase "heaven's artillery", means something from the sky that sounds like gunfire. This is the thunder.

9. D

In lines 19-20, Winona states that, if the storm does come closer, "the chances are a thousand to one against it hitting this particular house".

10. C

Line 23 states that "Winona's remarks might not be complimentary, but they were bracing". The fact that they weren't "complimentary" means they were 'critical'. The fact they were also "bracing" means they were 'invigorating'.

11. B

"lurid" and 'glaring' both mean 'unpleasantly bright'.

12. B

"pluck" and 'courage' both mean 'bravery'.

Test 31 — pages 132-135

1. C

Lines 2-3 state that "the dawn of the Space Age has seen huge amounts of man-made debris put into space". "dawn" refers to the beginning of something. Therefore, we can infer that space debris has been accumulating in space since the start of the Space Age.

2. A

Line 2 suggests that space debris can include "natural debris... such as rocks flying through space". Line 6 states it can also include "sections of old rockets" and "tiny pieces of shrapnel". There is no mention that operational satellites are classed as space debris, only "decommissioned" ones (line 5).

3. D

Lines 7-8 state that "around 670,000 pieces of debris are 1-10cm across, and a significant number (around 29,000) are larger". This shows that scientists have investigated the size of pieces of space debris.

4. B

Line 4 states that there are "over 170 million pieces of space debris". Lines 7-8 state that, out of 170 million pieces, "around 670,000 pieces of debris are 1-10 cm across, and a significant number (around 29,000) are larger". This means that most space debris must be under 1 cm across.

5. D

Line 10 states that Iridium 33 was "an operational US satellite". Line 11 states that the destroyed satellite was a "US communications satellite", meaning it was a satellite responsible for transmitting communications.

6. A

Lines 11-12 state that, as a consequence of the 2009 satellite collision, "thousands of debris shards" were created, and these posed "a greater and enduring threat" than the initial destruction of the operational satellite. Therefore, this increase in the amount of space debris orbiting earth was the main problem.

7. C

Lines 15-16 state that small pieces of space debris can't be monitored due to their "unpredictable orbits and sheer number".

8. D

Line 20 states that the damage was caused by "nothing more than a fleck of paint". The use of the phrase 'nothing more' implies that scientists were surprised that the piece of debris caused such obvious damage despite being so small.

9. A

Lines 23-24 state that most scientists think "there must be some intervention to ensure the problem is mitigated". This implies that scientists believe they must intervene to reduce the amount of space debris in orbit.

10. D

Lines 24-26 state that the idea of using lasers to cause space debris to fall to Earth is in its "planning stages", meaning lasers are not being used at the moment.

11. A

Line 24 describes the ideas as "Ingenious". "Ingenious" and 'innovative' both mean 'inventive'.

12. D

"functional" and 'usable' both mean 'in working order'.

Puzzles 11 — page 136

Travels Through Time

Leonardo: CONFIDENT   Albert: FEARFUL
Marie: EXCITED   Louis: CAUTIOUS
Isaac: PROUD   Ada: AMAZED
René: HESITANT   Erwin: FURIOUS
Niels: TEARFUL

The name of the historical figure is: CLEOPATRA

CGP

Verbal Reasoning:
Comprehension

The 11+
10-Minute Tests

For the CEM (Durham University) test

Book 2

Ages
10-11

Practise • Prepare • Pass
Everything your child needs for 11+ success

How to use this book

This book is made up of 10-minute tests and puzzle pages.
There are answers and detailed explanations in the pull-out section at the back of the book.

10-Minute Tests

- There are 31 tests in this book, each containing 12 questions.

- Each test is designed to target the type of comprehension questions that your child could come across in the verbal reasoning section of their 11+ test, and covers a variety of text types at the right difficulty level.

- Your child should aim to score around 10 or 11 out of 12 in each of the 10-minute tests.
  If they score less than this, use their results to work out the areas they need more practice on.

- If your child hasn't managed to finish the test in time, they need to work on increasing their speed, whereas if they have made a lot of mistakes, they need to work more carefully.

- Keep track of your child's scores using the progress chart on the inside back cover of the book.

Puzzle Pages

- There are 11 puzzle pages in this book, which are a great break from test-style questions. They encourage children to practise similar skills to those that they will need in the test, but in a fun way.

Published by CGP

Editors:
Emma Cleasby, Alex Fairer, Jack Perry, Holly Robinson, Sophie Scott

With thanks to Emma Cleasby, Alison Griffin and Jack Perry for the proofreading.

With thanks to Jan Greenway for the copyright research.

Extract from Angela Brazil's work printed with kind permission of Independent Age
(Registered Charity No. 210729) www.independentage.org

Please note that CGP is not associated with CEM or The University of Durham in any way.
This book does not include any official questions and it is not endorsed by CEM or The University of Durham.

CEM, Centre for Evaluation and Monitoring, Durham University and *The University of Durham*
are all trademarks of The University of Durham.

ISBN: 978 1 78294 769 1
Printed by Elanders Ltd, Newcastle upon Tyne
Clipart from Corel®

Based on the classic CGP style created by Richard Parsons.

Contents

You have **10 minutes** to do this test. Work as quickly and as accurately as you can.

Read this poem carefully and answer the questions that follow.

Upon the Sea

How many miles away it seems,
To my home upon the sea.
The crashing waves and battered cliffs
Are just a thought to me.
5   How much I long to go back
To my home upon the sea.

A childhood spent upon the waves,
A sail filled with a breeze.
My favourite things were a decent wind,
10 And the sight of millpond seas.
A simple life of sailing was,
A simple life of ease.

But now my life has moved me to,
Tall cities without end.
15 I live in a silent flat of stone,
Where walls don't creak or bend.
I long for my cabin of groaning wood,
And the rocking of my sapphire friend.

To hear his bellowing cry again
20 As he jumps upon the sand,
His ever-changing, whitened paws
Skirting along the land,
The salty lick that caresses my cheeks
As we travel hand in hand.

25 Out we'll go far beyond the coast,
Where giant cliffs seem but a line
That sits upon the golden waves,
Where the sun pursues to shine.
I'll rejoice in the heart of the sunlit sea,
30 Aboard my floating shrine.

I'll care not where it is I'm swept
Or if the seas turn grey,
Or if I'm tossed by turbulent hands
Into the thunderous fray,
35 Or if cotton clouds as black as pitch
Confuse the night and day.

And when my journey's days are spent,
And eternal sleep I face,
In this shifting, watery scene
40 I long to take my place,
So I'll stay upon the endless sea,
At rest in his blue embrace.

2

Answer these questions about the text that you've just read.
Circle the letter that matches the correct answer.

1. The first verse of the poem tells us that:
    A   the narrator would rather forget about the sea.
    B   the narrator thinks living by the sea is too noisy.
    C   the narrator doesn't often think about the sea.
    (D)   the narrator hasn't actually been to the sea for a long time.

2. What were the narrator's favourite things when they were a child?
    A   A strong gale and flat seas.
    B   A stiff breeze and calm seas.
    C   Very little wind and a sheltered bay.
    (D)   A light wind and the view of pools near the cliffs.

3. The narrator describes a life at sea as "simple" in lines 11-12?
   This suggests that:
    (A)   life at sea is uncomplicated.
    B   sailing is a skill that can be learnt by anyone.
    C   navigating the seas is easier than navigating on land.
    D   living on the sea could be quite boring.

4. Which of the following best describes where the narrator currently lives?
    (A)   In a small flat in a town.
    B   In a quiet location near a city.
    C   In a stone house in the countryside.
    D   In an apartment in an extensive city.

TURN OVER

5. What does "whitened paws" (line 21) refer to?

    A   The waves along the shoreline.

    Ⓑ   The feet of dogs on the beach.

    C   Small pebbles on the beach.

    D   The feet of people paddling in the shallows.

6. The narrator describes the cliffs as "but a line" (line 26). This suggests:

    A   they are a long way away.

    B   they are not very high.

    Ⓒ   they are incredibly sheer.

    D   there is little detail in the rock face.

7. Which of the following is described as a "floating shrine" (line 30)?

    A   A house

    B   The sea

    Ⓒ   A boat

    D   The sun

8. According to the poem, which of the following statements must be true?

    A   The narrator wishes to sail as part of a small crew.

    Ⓑ   The narrator doesn't mind where they sail to.

    C   The narrator wishes to often return to land.

    D   The narrator prefers sailing at night to sailing during the day.

9. Which of the following types of weather is not mentioned in the poem?

   A Storms
   B Sunshine ✓
   C Rain
   D Overcast

10. What does the narrator desire in lines 37-42?

   A To rest when they first reach land. ✓
   B To be buried at sea when they die.
   C To live on a boat when they retire.
   D To sleep when they've finished exploring the seas.

11. What does "caresses" (line 23) mean?

   A Holds ✗
   B Strikes
   C Nudges
   D Strokes

12. What does "eternal" (line 38) mean?

   A Endless ✓
   B Peaceful
   C Satisfying
   D Long

END OF TEST

7 / 12

You have **10 minutes** to do this test. Work as quickly and as accurately as you can.

Read this passage carefully and answer the questions that follow.

Hospital Trains

Although much less common now, hospital trains have played a vital role in the past, enabling wounded soldiers to be evacuated from war zones. The first use of hospital trains dates back to the Crimean War in the mid-19th century. During this war, English contractors built the Grand Crimean Central Railway so that trains laden
5 with ammunition and food could be used to supply the British army and its allies who were encamped in Russia. Although the main function of this railway was to transport provisions, it also became a way to extract wounded soldiers from scenes of conflict and deliver basic treatment to them on the move.

High numbers of casualties in World War I and World War II led to an increase
10 in the use and sophistication of hospital trains. Britain's fleet of hospital trains was expanded; normal passenger trains were stripped of their seats and modified to hold the basic facilities that medical staff would need to provide a range of treatments. A typical hospital train used in the Second World War often consisted of 14 carriages, able to carry around 360 patients. Behind the front engine, there was a long series of
15 carriages filled with beds which functioned as wards. The train also featured a large carriage that served as a rudimentary operating theatre and pharmacy. There were dedicated mess areas, where chefs cooked for staff and passengers.

The trains were manned by a team of trained nurses and Medical Officers who often had to work through the night to fulfil their duties. Workers known as orderlies
20 assisted medical staff in basic tasks, such as changing dressings and feeding the patients. They were also responsible for cleaning the train and fetching water. The staff lived aboard the train, working in the line of fire, often for months on end. They had to sleep in confined quarters and the wards quickly became smelly and crowded with wounded soldiers. Although patients were initially relieved to board a hospital
25 train and escape the conflict, the harsh reality on board meant many were thankful when the journey was over.

Answer these questions about the text that you've just read. Circle the letter that matches the correct answer.

1. What "vital role" (line 1) did hospital trains play during history?

    A   Providing armies fighting abroad with sufficient food and water.

 B   Dispatching trained doctors and nurses to war zones.

    C   Providing a way for soldiers to enter war zones to fight.

    (D)   Transporting injured servicemen away from the front line.

2. Which of the following best describes why the Grand Crimean Central Railway was built?

    A   To evacuate soldiers from war zones.

    (B)   To deliver supplies to British soldiers and their allies in Russia.

    C   To provide work for British railway contractors.

    D   To carry fresh ammunition for delivery to Russian soldiers.

3. Which of the following statements must be true?

    (A)   There are more hospital trains in use now than in the 1850s.

    (B)   The use of hospital trains declined between World War I and World War II.

    C   The number of hospital trains in service is slowly increasing.

    D   The number of active hospital trains was larger during World War II than during the Crimean War.

4. According to the text, which of the following facilities were not found on a hospital train during World War II?

    (A)   Artillery stores

    B   Kitchens

    C   Medicine stores

    D   Staff sleeping areas

TURN OVER ➡

5. According to the passage, the train staff "often had to work through the night to fulfil their duties" (line 19). What does this tell you?

    A   Many patients were not able to sleep during the night.

    B   Staff only worked during the night.

✓   Ⓒ   Many of the patients required round-the-clock care.

    D   Staff had to remain awake to drive the train.

6. Which of the following duties would you expect an orderly to perform?

    1.   Feeding patients

    2.   Dressing wounds

    3.   Cooking for staff

    4.   Performing operations

✗   A   1 and 2

    Ⓑ   1, 2 and 3

    C   1, 3 and 4

    D   2 and 4

7. According to the passage, staff on the hospital train were "working in the line of fire" (line 22). This means that:

    A   they could have been sacked at any moment.

✓   Ⓑ   they were in danger of being caught up in conflict.

    C   there was a risk that the train could catch fire.

    D   the areas they worked in were hot and unpleasant.

8. Which of the following words would you not use to describe the conditions on hospital trains?

✓   A   Perilous

    Ⓑ   Mouldy

    C   Fetid

    D   Cramped

9. Which of the following is not mentioned in the passage?

  A   The number of carriages a typical hospital train had during World War II.

  Ⓑ   How hospital trains were made for World War I and World War II.

✗ **C**   The number of staff serving on each hospital train in World War II.

  D   The patient capacity of a typical World War II hospital train.

10. Which of the following statements about patients' opinions of hospital trains is true?

  A   Patients expected hospital trains to be less comfortable than they were.

✓ **B**   Patients expected the journeys to be shorter than they were.

  C   Patients overestimated how much treatment they'd receive on the trains.

  Ⓓ   Patients didn't think conditions aboard hospital trains would be as unpleasant as they were.

11. What does "rudimentary" (line 16) mean?

  A   Clear

✓ Ⓑ   Crude

  C   Small

  D   Unfussy

12. What does "confined" (line 23) mean?

  Ⓐ   Restricted

  B   Deficient

✓ **C**   Dingy

  D   Squalid

END OF TEST

1 . / 12

You have **10 minutes** to do this test. Work as quickly and as accurately as you can.

Read this passage carefully and answer the questions that follow.

An abridged extract from 'The Moonstone'

The question of how I am to start the story properly I have tried to settle in two ways. First, by scratching my head, which led to nothing. Second, by consulting my daughter Penelope, which has resulted in an entirely new idea.

Penelope's notion is that I should set down what happened, regularly day by day,
5 beginning with the day when we got the news that Mr. Franklin Blake was expected on a visit to the house. The only difficulty is to fetch out the dates, in the first place. This Penelope offers to do for me by looking into her own diary, which she was taught to keep when she was at school, and which she has gone on keeping ever since. In answer to an improvement on this notion, devised by myself, namely, that
10 she should tell the story instead of me, out of her own diary, Penelope observes, with a fierce look and a red face, that her journal is for her own private eye, and that no living creature shall ever know what is in it but herself.

Beginning, then, on Penelope's plan, I beg to mention that I was specially called one Wednesday morning into my lady's own sitting-room, the date being the
15 twenty-fourth of May, Eighteen hundred and forty-eight.

"Gabriel," says my lady, "here is news that will surprise you. Franklin Blake has come back from abroad. He has been staying with his father in London, and he is coming to us to-morrow to stop till next month, and keep Rachel's birthday."

If I had had a hat in my hand, nothing but respect would have prevented me from
20 throwing that hat up to the ceiling. I had not seen Mr. Franklin since he was a boy, living along with us in this house. He was, out of all sight (as I remember him), the nicest boy that ever spun a top or broke a window. Miss Rachel, who was present, and to whom I made that remark, observed, in return, that SHE remembered him as the most atrocious tyrant that ever tortured a doll, and the hardest driver of an
25 exhausted little girl in string harness that England could produce.

Wilkie Collins

Answer these questions about the text that you've just read.
Circle the letter that matches the correct answer.

1. What is the first thing that the narrator does when deciding how to start his story?

   A   Consults his diary.

   B   Asks his family for ideas.

   C   Tries to come up with a solution by himself.

   D   Gathers research using other books.

2. At what point does Penelope think the narrator should begin his story?

   A   The day Mr. Blake arrives at the house.

   B   The evening of the 24th May.

   C   When he left school.

   D   The day he receives news of Mr. Blake's arrival.

3. According to the text, the narrator suggests that Penelope should "tell the story instead of me, out of her own diary" (line 10). Why does Penelope not agree to this?

   A   She doesn't want anyone to hear what is written in her diary.

   B   She does not want the narrator to copy her version of the story.

   C   Her journal is to only be seen by her and her closest friends.

   D   She is worried the narrator will tell other people what is in the diary.

4. Which of the following statements must be true?

   A   The narrator has not seen Franklin for a long time.

   B   Penelope has only recently started keeping a diary.

   C   Penelope and Rachel are sisters.

   D   Franklin has never visited the house before.

TURN OVER ➡️

5. During which of the following months could Rachel's birthday fall?

    A   April

    (B)   June

✓   C   July

    D   September

6. Which of the following is not true of Mr. Franklin?

    A   He has spent some of his adult life in foreign countries.

✓   B   He spent some of his childhood with Rachel.

    C   He has family living in London.

    (D)   He is intending on staying at the house indefinitely.

7. The narrator states that he would throw a hat "up to the ceiling" (line 20) if he
✓   had one. What does this suggest?

    A   He is delighted that it will soon be Rachel's birthday.

    B   He wishes to take his hat off as a sign of respect to his employer.

    (C)   He is excited at the prospect of Mr. Franklin's arrival.

    D   He is disappointed that Mr. Franklin is no longer abroad.

✓
8. Which of the following is not mentioned in the text?

    (A)   The location of the house in relation to London.

    B   The relationship between the narrator and Penelope.

    C   The name of the narrator.

    D   The year when the story the narrator is trying to write is set.

9. Which of the following best describes how the narrator remembers Mr. Franklin?

   A   Playful and mischievous

✓   **B**   Charming and well-behaved

   C   Agreeable and quiet

   D   Sullen and accident-prone

10. Which of the following best describes Mr. Franklin's conduct according to Rachel?

✗   **A**   Indifferent   *objectionable /atrocious*

   B   Cynical

   C   Objectionable

   D   Affable

11. What does "devised" (line 9) mean?

✓   **A**   Imagined

   B   Conceived

   C   Initiated

   D   Prompted

12. In the context of the passage, what does "tyrant" (line 24) mean?

✓   **A**   Bully

   B   Ruler

   C   Trickster

   D   Rebel

END OF TEST

11 / 12

Time for a break! This puzzle is a great way to practise your **comprehension** skills.

Pony Club Problems

Tina is reporting on the recent Dewsman Cup, a prestigious horse race.
She takes some notes while at the race. Using Tina's notes, work out:

- which order the four horses (Bullseye, Jupiter, Dasher and Pickles) came in.
- which rider (Harriet, Serena, Benjamin and Jack) was riding each horse.
- what colour jersey (Red, Yellow, Green and Blue) each rider was wearing.

Fill in the grid below with ticks and crosses to help you keep track of what you know. The information from the first clue has already been filled in for you.

Tina's Notes

- The rider who came first was wearing a yellow jersey.
- Bullseye, the second place horse, was ridden by a girl.
- Harriet, who didn't win, was one place in front of Benjamin.
- Dasher was ridden by a boy in a blue jersey.
- Jupiter came two places behind Pickles.
- Jupiter's rider wore red.
- Jack was two places behind the person who rode Bullseye.

	Harriet	Serena	Benjamin	Jack	Red	Yellow	Green	Blue	1st	2nd	3rd	4th
Bullseye												
Jupiter												
Dasher												
Pickles												
1st					✗	✓	✗	✗				
2nd						✗						
3rd						✗						
4th						✗						
Red												
Yellow												
Green												
Blue												

1st place: Horse: _____   Rider: _____   Jersey: __Yellow__

2nd place: Horse: _____   Rider: _____   Jersey: _____

3rd place: Horse: _____   Rider: _____   Jersey: _____

4th place: Horse: _____   Rider: _____   Jersey: _____

You have **10 minutes** to do this test. Work as quickly and as accurately as you can.

Read this passage carefully and answer the questions that follow.

An abridged extract from 'The Three Musketeers'

D'Artagnan, in a state of fury, crossed the antechamber at three bounds, and was darting toward the stairs, which he reckoned upon descending four at a time, when he ran against a Musketeer* who was coming out of one of M. de Treville's private rooms.

"Excuse me," said d'Artagnan, endeavouring to resume his course, "I am in a hurry."

5 Scarcely had he descended the first stair, when a hand of iron seized him by the belt.

"You are in a hurry?" said the Musketeer, as pale as a sheet. "Under that pretence you run against me! You say, 'Excuse me,' and you believe that is sufficient? Do you fancy because you have heard Monsieur** de Treville speak to us a little cavalierly today that other people are to treat us as he speaks to us?"

10 "My faith!" replied d'Artagnan, recognising Athos. "I did not do it intentionally, and I said 'Excuse me.' This is quite enough. Leave your hold, then, I beg of you."

"Monsieur," said Athos, letting him go, "you are not polite; it is easy to perceive that you come from a distance."

D'Artagnan had already strode down three or four stairs, but at Athos's last remark he
15 stopped short.

"Monsieur!" said he, "however far I may come, it is not you who can give me a lesson in good manners. Ah! If I were not running after someone."

"Monsieur Man-in-a-hurry, you can find me without running — ME, you understand?"

"At what hour?"

20 "About noon."

"Good!" cried d'Artagnan, "I will be there ten minutes before twelve." And he set off running as if the devil possessed him, hoping that he might yet find the stranger, whose slow pace could not have carried him far.

Alexandre Dumas

* Musketeer — *a member of the 17th and 18th century French royal guard*
** Monsieur — *a form of address meaning Mr. or Sir*

TURN OVER ➡

1. The extract says d'Artagnan "crossed the antechamber at three bounds" (line 1).
    This tells us that:

    A   D'Artagnan has very long legs.

    B   D'Artagnan crossed the room in three big hops.

    C   D'Artagnan strode across the room very quickly.

    D   The antechamber was three metres wide.

2. What does "reckoned upon" (line 2) mean in the context of the passage?

    A   Counted

    B   Anticipated

    C   Justified

    D   Quantified

3. Why does Athos seize d'Artagnan in line 5?

    A   He is trying to stop d'Artagnan from falling downstairs.

    B   He wants to take d'Artagnan back to Monsieur de Treville.

    C   He wants to get revenge against d'Artagnan.

    D   He wants to force d'Artagnan to explain himself.

4. Why is Athos "as pale as a sheet" (line 6) when he first speaks to d'Artagnan?

    A   He is angry at d'Artagnan.

    B   He has naturally pale features.

    C   He is wearing pale-coloured clothing.

    D   He is feeling unwell.

5. Which of the following must be true about Monsieur de Treville and Athos?

   A   Monsieur de Treville and Athos are equals.

   B   Athos doesn't respect Monsieur de Treville.

   C   Monsieur de Treville has behaved terribly towards Athos.

   D   Athos is more forgiving of Monsieur de Treville than he is of d'Artagnan.

6. Which of the following statements about Athos and d'Artagnan is false?

   A   D'Artagnan goes out of his way to annoy Athos.

   B   Athos holds a degree of power over d'Artagnan.

   C   Athos and d'Artagnan are at odds.

   D   D'Artagnan thinks that Athos is over-reacting.

7. According to Athos, what does d'Artagnan's supposed impoliteness say about him?

   A   He doesn't respect the position of the musketeers.

   B   He comes from somewhere else where manners aren't as refined.

   C   He is too young to have learnt good manners.

   D   He is in too much of a hurry to be polite to Athos.

8. According to the text, d'Artagnan "stopped short" (line 15) while descending the stairs. Why does he do this?

   A   Athos's last remark offends d'Artagnan.

   B   D'Artagnan misheard Athos's last remark.

   C   Athos's last remark impresses d'Artagnan.

   D   Athos's last remark challenges d'Artagnan to a duel.

TURN OVER ➡

9. According to the text, why is d'Artagnan in a hurry?

    A   He is angry and wants to get away from the antechamber.

    B   He is late to meet someone.

    (C)   He is trying to catch up with someone.

    D   Someone is chasing after him.

10. Which of the following is false about d'Artagnan?

    (A)   He has no desire to retaliate against Athos.

    B   He would have dealt with Athos differently if he hadn't been in a hurry.

    C   He believes that Athos has no valid reason to be offended.

    D   He finds Athos to be very impolite.

11. D'Artagnan says that he will arrive for his noon meeting with Athos at "ten minutes before twelve" (line 21). This tells us that:

    A   D'Artagnan is worried about missing the meeting.

    B   D'Artagnan is unable to tell the time properly.

    (C)   D'Artagnan is assuring Athos that he will turn up.

    D   D'Artagnan isn't available to meet at noon.

12. What does "endeavouring" (line 4) mean?

    A   Toiling

    (B)   Striving

    C   Pursuing

    D   Persevering

END OF TEST

/ 12

You have **10 minutes** to do this test. Work as quickly and as accurately as you can.

Read this passage carefully and answer the questions that follow.

Labyrinths and Mazes

Mazes have inspired and frustrated people for thousands of years. They offer a series
of bewildering choices, forcing those who enter to select the correct route to the centre.
   A huge variety of traditional and more wacky mazes exist today. Built around 1691
for England's reigning monarch, William III, Hampton Court maze is the world's oldest
5 hedge maze and consists of half a mile of paths. On the edge of London, it's one of the
most popular mazes in the world, taking the average visitor between 30 to 45 minutes to
complete. Though the layout of this maze hasn't changed since its construction, in 1960
the original hornbeam tree hedges were replaced by yew trees and 46 years later, an
audio exhibit called *Trace* was installed. This high-tech addition entertains visitors with
10 mysterious sounds that are triggered to play by motion sensors. This maze is dwarfed
however by the hedge maze at Longleat, in Wiltshire, which holds the title as the world's
longest. It features 1.5 miles of path flanked by yew trees and can take up to 90 minutes
to solve. Visitors to this stately home and estate can also attempt King Arthur's Mirror
Maze, a futuristic maze featuring glass mirrors and lighting effects.
15   Labyrinths are a close relation of mazes. They present a single route, which leads to
the centre and back out again, which visitors merely have to follow. Many labyrinths
exist today, such as that on the floor of Chartres Cathedral. This 13th-century labyrinth
is made from tiles, laid into a 260-metre-long pathway. Historians have hypothesised
such labyrinths may have been used to symbolise the sole path to salvation. Modern
20 churches have used labyrinths in similar ways too. In 2000, St Paul's Cathedral featured
a temporary labyrinth, painted on canvas, that encouraged people who followed the
route to reflect and pray.
   Turf labyrinths are made by creating shallow trench-like paths in lawned areas. The
largest of Britain's 8 surviving turf labyrinths is located at Saffron Walden. It was built in
25 the late 1600s and has a 132-foot diameter. Its mile-long pathway loops 17 times and
still delights visitors today.

TURN OVER ➡

Answer these questions about the text that you've just read.
Circle the letter that matches the correct answer.

1. Approximately how old was the maze at Hampton Court when *Trace* was introduced?

   A   46 years old

   B   269 years old

   C   300 years old

   D   315 years old

2. Which of the following statements best describes Longleat?

   A   A private mansion and country estate.

   B   A manor house with grounds that are open to the public.

   C   An area of countryside featuring a number of mazes.

   D   A long and complicated hedge maze.

3. Which of the following materials is not mentioned in relation to labyrinths?

   A   Grass

   B   Canvas

   C   Trees

   D   Floor tiles

4. How much longer is the hedge maze at Longleat than at Hampton Court?

   A   Four times as long.

   B   Three times as long.

   C   Twice as long.

   D   Half as long.

5. Which of the following words does not describe the maze at Hampton Court?

   A   Updated

   B   Admired

   C   Obsolete

   D   Historic

6. Which of the following is not mentioned by the text?

   A   The location of the world's longest hedge maze.

   B   Who Hampton Court maze was built for.

   C   The potential meaning of Christian labyrinths.

   D   The total area covered by the largest turf labyrinth in England.

7. According to the text, what is the difference between mazes and labyrinths?

   A   Labyrinths are slightly older than mazes.

   B   Labyrinths have more confusing paths than mazes.

   C   Solving mazes involves making decisions whereas solving labyrinths doesn't.

   D   The paths through mazes always lead to the centre, whereas the paths through labyrinths don't.

8. According to the text, which of the following must be true?

   A   Hampton Court maze is made from hornbeam tree hedges.

   B   Most historic British turf labyrinths have a diameter of under 132 feet.

   C   Longleat House maze is easier to complete than Hampton Court maze.

   D   King Arthur's Mirror Maze is in Edinburgh.

TURN OVER ➡

9. Which of the following is the oldest?

    A   Hampton Court maze

    B   Longleat House hedge maze

    C   Saffron Walden turf labyrinth

    D   Chartres Cathedral labyrinth

10. Which of the following features is shared by both the hedge maze at Hampton Court and the hedge maze at Longleat?

    A   The material the walls of the mazes are made of.

    B   The number of visitors attracted per year.

    C   The height of the maze walls.

    D   The reason why they were built.

11. According to the text, which of the following must be false?

    A   The labyrinth at Saffron Walden was built at the end of the 17th century.

    B   Some labyrinths may have religious meaning.

    C   The labyrinth at St Paul's Cathedral can still be visited today.

    D   You enter a labyrinth the same way you exit it.

12. Which of the following contains the longest distance of pathways?

    A   Longleat House hedge maze

    B   Chartres Cathedral labyrinth

    C   Saffron Walden turf labyrinth

    D   Hampton Court maze

END OF TEST

/ 12

Puzzles 2

Time for a break! This puzzle is a great way to practise your **word-making** skills.

Stepping Stone Maze

Ellie wants to reach the dark blue stone. She must follow a path of words that mean the **centre** of something. She can move one stone at a time in any direction. Each stone can only be used once. Draw a line showing her route, filling in the words below as you go. The first word has been done for you.

K E R N E L ___ ___ ___ ___ ___ ___ ___ ___   ___ ___ ___   ___ ___ ___ ___ ___ ___

___ ___ ___ ___ ___   ___ ___ ___   ___ ___ ___ ___ ___ ___   ___ ___ ___ ___

You have **10 minutes** to do this test. Work as quickly and as accurately as you can.

Read this passage carefully and answer the questions that follow.

Sign Language

In addition to lip-reading, many of those who are deaf or hearing-impaired use sign languages when communicating. Sign languages comprise hand gestures that signify certain words or sounds. Other vital components include facial expressions, body language and fingerspelling, which consists of signing letters using hand movements.

5 Signing has existed in Britain for hundreds of years but it wasn't until 1760 that a formal system was developed by Thomas Braidwood, a teacher at a deaf school in Britain. He classified the signs he used to converse with his pupils to develop the 'combined system', the predecessor of British Sign Language (BSL), the sign language used in the UK today. Braidwood also trained his nephew, Joseph Watson, in the

10 'combined system'. Watson went onto become the headmaster of another school for the deaf in Britain, developing and advocating the combined system.

Despite these early advances, ignorance about the values of a formal sign language prevailed throughout much of the 19th and 20th centuries. Use of signing was actively discouraged in the majority of British schools and signers were forced to

15 fingerspell or lip-read instead. However, attitudes changed in the 1970s. BSL, which had been developing in deaf communities over time and had started to be formalised in the 'combined system', began to be taken more seriously as a language and was increasingly taught in schools. BSL was recognised as an official language in 2003.

Today, sign languages are used across the world. Though some countries share

20 spoken languages, there are huge variations between national sign languages. For example, though Britain and America share a verbal language, American Sign Language is almost unintelligible to BSL users. There are also regional differences within national sign languages. These divergences are akin to dialects, variants of verbal languages where certain words and accents differ. Some sign languages do share similarities

25 however. Auslan (an Australia sign language) and New Zealand Sign Language are closely related to BSL. These languages originated in the 19th century when British settlers introduced their native sign languages to Australia and New Zealand.

1. According to the text, which of the following is not a key part of sign language?

    A   Facial expressions

    (B)   Blinking   ✓

    C   Fingerspelling

    D   Hand movements

2. Which of the following statements about Joseph Watson is false?

    (A)   He was one of the first people to teach BSL in a school.

    B   He was related to Thomas Braidwood.   ✓

    C   At some point, he worked in a different school to Thomas Braidwood.

    D   He helped to pioneer 'the combined system'.

3. Which of the following statements best describes 'the combined system'?

    (A)   An advanced version of British Sign Language.
            PROFESSOR.
    B   A forerunner of British Sign Language.

    C   A system developed for use in Braidwood's school alone.

    D   A primitive sign language involving lip-reading and fingerspelling.

4. According to the text, why did many British schools discourage the use
    of sign language?

    A   People outside the deaf community didn't know that signing existed.

    (B)   People didn't fully understand the benefits of signing.   ✓

    C   People preferred to learn sign language outside of school.

    D   Schools didn't understand what signing was used for.

TURN OVER ➡

5. Which of the following best describes the development of British Sign Language?

    A   Simplistic

    B   Radical

    C   Immediate

    (D)   Collaborative   ✓

6. Which of the following statements about sign language must be true?

    A   Sign languages are only used by those in deaf communities.

    (B)   An official sign language was recognised in Britain under 50 years ago.

    C   British Sign Language has developed more than any other sign language.

    D   Sign language has only ever been taught in schools exclusively for those who are deaf.

    ✓

7. How did attitudes towards British Sign Language change in the 1970s?

    A   People found BSL easier to learn that the 'combined system'.

    B   BSL gained official recognition as a language.

    (C)   More people saw BSL as a valid form of communication.

    D   People started to think BSL should replace lip-reading.

    ✓

8. Which of the following sign languages would you not expect to share many features with British Sign Language?

    A   American Sign Language ✓ .

    (B)   New Zealand Sign Language ✗   ?

    C   Auslan ✗

    D   The combined system ✗

9. Which of the following statements about BSL must be true?

    A   British Sign Language isn't widely known.

    B   British signers use obscure signs that are hard to interpret.   ?

    C   British Sign Language is unlike any other sign language.   '

    D   British Sign Language isn't spoken in all English-speaking countries. ✓.

10. In the context of the passage, what does "variants of verbal languages" (line 23) refer to?

    A   Languages spoken in different countries.

    B   Local versions of spoken languages.

    C   Regional sign languages.

    D   Lip-reading and fingerspelling.

11. What does the word "components" (line 3) mean?

    A   Fragments

    B   Elements

    C   Modules

    D   Sections

12. What does the word "divergences" (line 23) mean?

    A   Deviations

    B   Disputes

    C   Altercations

    D   Dissensions

END OF TEST

6. / 12

You have **10 minutes** to do this test. Work as quickly and as accurately as you can.

> Read this passage carefully and answer the questions that follow.

The Inventor

Anya walked quickly, hoping to reach the Inventor's house before the sun slipped behind the castle. She headed east of the castle and crossed a bridge leading to the Havoc, a twisting warren of ramshackle houses occupied by the poorest citizens. At first, Anya had found the Havoc bewildering, often tramping around its grimy
5 cobbled passageways for what felt like hours in search of the Inventor's dwelling, only to find herself right back at the bridge in the shadow of the castle's eastern wall. Now, she knew those streets as well as her own.

The sun dipped below the horizon just as Anya arrived at the Inventor's house. Her spirits lifted as soon as she saw his ornate door. She noticed wispy tendrils of
10 smoke rising from the chimney and smiled. The Inventor always kept a roaring fire, though Anya didn't know how he afforded such a luxury, given his address.

"Sorry I'm late!" Anya called out as she crossed the threshold into the warmth. She hurriedly shut out the chilly evening air and headed for the back room. The Inventor was always ensconced there, tinkering away with a delicate, shining piece
15 of the invention or puzzling over a conundrum in his velvet armchair.

Anya had barely entered the room when the Inventor reproached her.

"Where have you been?" he cried in a fit of uncharacteristic impatience. "I need to show you something!" Before Anya could protest, the Inventor had bustled her over to the mahogany table where the gleaming invention lay. "Look! I think..."
20 The Inventor's excitement was palpable, and Anya couldn't help but be infected by it as she inspected the intricate, silver machine that had been his obsession for as long as she'd known him. It looked exactly as it had the previous day, though a narrow spindle now protruded from its centre. Anya traced her finger along it.

As soon as she made contact, the invention began to revolve, its polished surfaces
25 reflecting many-hued flashes of firelight around the room. Anya and the Inventor looked on in awe at his exquisite creation.

"It's finally finished, Anya," he sighed, finally at ease.

Answer these questions about the text that you've just read.
Circle the letter that matches the correct answer.

1. Which of the following best describes the Havoc?

    A   Obscure

    B   Mangled

    C   Garbled

    D   Disorientating

2. The narrator tells us that Anya knows the streets of the Havoc "as well as her own" (line 7). This tells us that:

    A   Anya has lived in the Havoc in the past.

    B   Anya currently lives somewhere other than in the Havoc.

    C   the streets of the Havoc are similar to other parts of the city.

    D   Anya has always found it easy to negotiate the streets in the Havoc.

3. What time of day is it when Anya reaches the Inventor's house?

    A   Just before dawn

    B   Early afternoon

    C   Around dusk

    D   Just before midnight

4. Why is Anya surprised that the Inventor always keeps "a roaring fire" (line 10)?

    A   Only the richest people in the city are allowed to have fires.

    B   Wood is more expensive in the Havoc than in other parts of the city.

    C   It's rare for anyone in the city to be able to afford even a meagre fire.

    D   She assumes that he is too poor to afford firewood because he lives in a poor area of town.

TURN OVER ➡

5. Why does the Inventor chastise Anya for being late?

    A   He desperately wants to share something with her.

    B   He's been waiting to work on the invention with her.

    C   He's not a very patient man.

    D   He was worried that she'd got lost in the Havoc.

6. Which of the following best describes the appearance of the invention?

    A   Mundane

    B   Lustrous

    C   Blinding

    D   Kaleidoscopic

7. The author tells us the "Inventor's excitement was palpable" (line 20). What does this mean?

    A   The Inventor's excitement was so strong that Anya could almost feel it.

    B   The Inventor's excitement was unnecessarily excessive.

    C   The Inventor was visibly shaking with excitement.

    D   The Inventor was trying to hide his excitement.

8. Which of the following is not mentioned in the passage?

    A   The location of the Havoc in relation to the castle.

    B   The place where the Inventor works on the invention.

    C   The day on which Anya last visited the Inventor.

    D   The exact length of time the Inventor has taken to complete the invention.

9. Which of the following statements about Anya is false?

A   The Inventor trusts Anya with the invention.

B   Anya looks forward to visiting the Inventor.

C   Anya isn't very familiar with the details of the invention.

D   Anya visits the Inventor quite frequently.

10. Which of the following best describes how the Inventor feels once he has seen the invention in motion?

A   He is inspired to continue working on the invention.

B   He is relieved to have finished the invention.

C   He finds the invention a little terrifying.

D   He isn't very happy with what the invention does.

11. What does the word "ensconced" (line 14) mean?

A   Ensnared

B   Settled

C   Confined

D   Reclined

12. What does the word "protruded" (line 23) mean?

A   Projected

B   Penetrated

C   Escalated

D   Expanded

END OF TEST

/ 12

You have **10 minutes** to do this test. Work as quickly and as accurately as you can.

Read this passage carefully and answer the questions that follow.

An extract from 'The Sea Fairies'

Absolute silence reigned in the silver passage. No fish were there; not even a sea flower grew to relieve the stern grandeur of this vast corridor. Trot began to be impressed with the fact that she was a good way from her home and mother, and she wondered if she would ever get back again to the white cottage on the cliff. Here
5   she was, at the bottom of the great ocean, swimming through a big tunnel that had an enchanted castle at the end, and a group of horrible sea devils at the other! In spite of this thought, she was not very much afraid. Although two fairy mermaids were her companions, she relied, strange to say, more upon her tried and true friend, Cap'n Bill, than upon her newer acquaintances to see her safely out of her present
10   trouble.

Cap'n Bill himself did not feel very confident.

"I don't care two cents* what becomes o' me," he told Princess Clia in a low voice, "but I'm drea'ful worried over our Trot. She's too sweet an' young to be made an end of in this 'ere fashion."
15   Clia smiled at this speech. "I'm sure you will find the little girl's end a good way off," she replied. "Trust to our powerful queen, and be sure she will find some means for us all to escape uninjured."

The light grew brighter as they advanced, until finally they perceived a magnificent archway just ahead of them. Aquareine hesitated a moment whether to
20   go on or turn back, but there was no escaping the sea devils behind them, and she decided the best way out of their difficulties was to bravely face the unknown Zog** and rely upon her fairy powers to prevent his doing any mischief to herself or her friends. So she led the way, and together they approached the archway and passed through it.

L. Frank Baum

* cents — *coins roughly equivalent to pennies*
** Zog — *an evil magician who is part-man, part-monster*

Answer these questions about the text that you've just read.
Circle the letter that matches the correct answer.

1. Which of the following best describes the "vast corridor" (line 2)?

   A   Flamboyant

   B   Infinite

   C   Diminutive

   D   Austere

2. Where is the "vast corridor" (line 2) located?

   A   At the end of a passage

   B   Underneath a cliff

   C   In the depths of the sea

   D   In an enchanted castle under the ocean

3. According to the passage, "Trot began to be impressed with the fact that she was a good way from her home and mother" (lines 2-3). What does this tell us?

   A   Trot is relieved that the way back to her house is easy to navigate.

   B   Trot has started to think about how far from home she is.

   C   Trot has just learned how far away from home she is.

   D   Trot is happy to have some independence from her mother.

4. Why is Trot "swimming through a big tunnel" (line 5)?

   A   She is trying to get to the enchanted castle.

   B   It leads back to the white cottage on the cliff.

   C   She is being driven forward by evil creatures.

   D   Zog is chasing her.

TURN OVER ➡

5. According to the text, who does Trot trust to protect her the most?

    A   Cap'n Bill

    B   Princess Clia

    C   Aquareine

    D   Herself

6. Which of the following statements about Cap'n Bill and Trot are true?

    1.   Trot has known Cap'n Bill for longer than she's known Aquareine.

    2.   Cap'n Bill prioritises Trot's safety over his own.

    3.   Cap'n Bill thinks that Trot is too weak to survive their ordeal.

    4.   Cap'n Bill feels responsible for Trot.

    A   1 and 2

    B   1 and 3

    C   1, 2 and 3

    D   1, 2 and 4

7. Cap'n Bill speaks in a "low voice" (lines 12-13) when discussing Trot's safety with Clia. This means that:

    A   Cap'n Bill is unsure whether to confide in Clia.

    B   Cap'n Bill is speaking in a sad tone.

    C   The pitch of Cap'n Bill's voice was unusually low.

    D   Cap'n Bill doesn't want anyone to overhear him confiding in Clia.

8. Which of the following best describes Clia?

    A   Loyal

    B   Indecisive

    C   Reckless

    D   Deft

9. Why does Aquareine hesitate before going through the archway?

    A   She isn't sure if she's going in the right direction.

    B   She is worried that there are sea devils on the other side.

    C   She knows that they'll have to face Zog on the other side.

    D   She knows she can't protect her friends once she passes through it.

10. Who is in charge of the party?

    A   Bill

    B   Aquareine

    C   Clia

    D   Trot

11. In the context of the passage, what does "reigned" (line 1) mean?

    A   Prevailed

    B   Controlled

    C   Constrained

    D   Administered

12. What does "relieve" (line 2) mean?

    A   Replace

    B   Subdue

    C   Dominate

    D   Soften

END OF TEST

/ 12

Time for a break! This puzzle is a great way to practise your **spelling** skills.

Dastardly Directions

A robber has written a set of directions to his hideout,
but only the instructions that have no spelling mistakes can be trusted.
Starting at the point shown by the arrow, face **north** and follow the correct directions.
Circle the hideout on the map and underline any mistakes in the instructions.

1. Follow the rout to the south gait.

2. Go forwards until you reach the bakery on the left.

3. Turn left at the bakery and go up the street until you reach a statue.

4. Go passed the statue and entrance the street that has a house.

5. Turn left, follow the road to the gate and go through it. Go left until you reach a stream and follow it north-west.

6. Go strait ahead, folowing the stream untill you see a bridge.

7. Cross the bridge, go left and follow the west side off the streem.

8. Keep walking until you reach the second fork in the stream.

9. Swim to the over side of the stream and head past the littel farm.

10. Turn right at the mill and head to the cave. You've found the hideout!

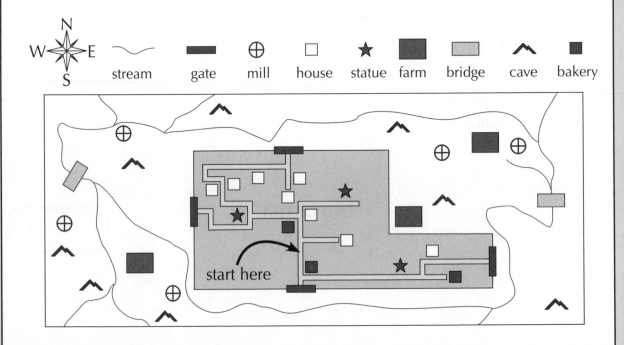

36

Test 9

You have **10 minutes** to do this test. Work as quickly and as accurately as you can.

> Read this passage carefully and answer the questions that follow.

Maestro!

The roar of the 5000-strong audience sitting beneath the domed roof thrilled Mateo. He couldn't believe it — his debut at Salburn's most prestigious venue, on the closing night of the 250th Summer Festival at that! He dared to poke his head through the curtains to admire the auditorium. It was very different to the venues he normally
5 played. The audience was just over double the size of the crowd at his last solo concert in the Reitzen Theatre.

Since the first annual Summer Festival in 1768, music lovers have been flocking to Salburn in late July to enjoy two weeks of concerts from some of the world's most eminent musicians. This year, Mateo had heard a breathtaking recital of Handel's
10 *Messiah* at the Vienno Cathedral that had eclipsed everything he'd seen in previous years. It featured some of his peers from his days studying abroad in Filben. Today, however, he had shut himself away in the practice rooms of the Royal Music School, overlooking the Cathedral. Despite the hot August weather, he'd spent four hours at his piano, perfecting the complex concerto.

15 Just as Mateo was taking in the occupants of the boxes in the hall, Carla Piento walked into the wings. As a fellow Filben Conservatoire graduate and seasoned performer in the Salene Opera House, she knew the ropes. He'd learnt a great deal playing for her.

"Pronto?" she asked in her native tongue. Mateo's Italian was poor, so he just
20 nodded in response, but he did not feel ready at all. He was suddenly gripped with apprehension. The lights of the grand room dimmed and a hushed silence descended.

As a spotlight rose on the stage, Carla strode forwards. She bowed low and turned to face the orchestra, taking the baton from the conductor's stand and grabbing the first violin's attention. But the orchestra was awaiting one final member. Mateo took a deep
25 breath and walked onto the stage to the sound of applause. He couldn't help but beam with delight.

TURN OVER ➡

Answer these questions about the text that you've just read.
Circle the letter that matches the correct answer.

1. When does Mateo's concert at the Salburn Summer Festival take place?

   A   August 1768

   B   July 1968

   C   July 2018

   D   August 2017

2. According to the text, what is the likely number of people who attended Mateo's concert at the Reitzen Theatre?

   A   Approximately 5000 people

   B   Over 2500 people

   C   Just under 2500 people

   D   Around 2000 people

3. Which of the following is not in Salburn?

   A   The Filben Conservatoire

   B   The Royal Music School

   C   The Salene Opera House

   D   Vienno Cathedral

4. Which of the following statements about Mateo is false?

   A   Mateo has performed in the Salene Opera House before.

   B   Mateo has played both in orchestras and on his own.

   C   Mateo has worked with Carla Piento on previous occasions.

   D   Mateo has attended the Summer Festival in the past.

5. What does Carla Piento mean when she asks "Pronto?" (line 19)?

   A   "Are you nervous?"

   B   "Are you ready?"

   C   "Do you have your music?"

   D   "Is the show about to start?"

6. Which of the following statements must be false?

   A   The Salene Opera House is famed for its acoustics.

   B   The Salene Opera House is only used during the Summer Festival.

   C   The Salene Opera House is over 250 years old.

   D   All musical performances at the Summer Festival are held in the
        Salene Opera House.

7. According to the text, Carla Piento "knew the ropes" (line 17). This means:

   A   she has performed the piece they are due to perform many times.

   B   she often helps out back-stage at the Salene Opera House.

   C   she has lots of experience performing at the Salene Opera House.

   D   she knows every detail of the layout of the auditorium.

8. According to the text, which of the following is not mentioned as a feature of the
   Salene Opera House?

   A   A vaulted ceiling

   B   Private practice rooms

   C   A stage

   D   Individual boxes for spectators

TURN OVER ➡

9. What is Carla Piento's profession?

    A   Conductor

    B   Music critic

    C   Opera singer

    D   Violinist

10. Which of the following is not mentioned in the text?

    A   The instrument which Mateo plays.

    B   The nationality of Carla Piento.

    C   The name of the piece Mateo is due to perform.

    D   The length of the Summer Festival.

11. Which of the following emotions are not experienced by Mateo during the passage?

    A   Anxiety

    B   Exhilaration

    C   Glee

    D   Awkwardness

12. What does "eminent" (line 9) mean?

    A   Academic

    B   Illustrious

    C   Popular

    D   Talented

END OF TEST

/ 12

You have **10 minutes** to do this test. Work as quickly and as accurately as you can.

Read this poem carefully and answer the questions that follow.

An abridged version of 'A Prisoner In A Dungeon Deep'

A prisoner in a dungeon deep
Sat musing silently;
His head was rested on his hand,
His elbow on his knee.

5 Turned he his thoughts to future times
Or are they backward cast?
For freedom is he pining now
Or mourning for the past?

No, he has lived so long enthralled
10 Alone in dungeon gloom
That he has lost regret and hope,
Has ceased to mourn his doom.

He pines not for the light of day
Nor sighs for freedom now;
15 Such weary thoughts have ceased at length
To rack his burning brow.

Lost in a maze of wandering thoughts
He sits unmoving there;
That posture and that look proclaim
20 The stupor of despair.

Yet not for ever did that mood
Of sullen calm prevail;
There was a something in his eye
That told another tale.

25 It did not speak of reason gone,
It was not madness quite;
It was a fitful flickering fire,
A strange uncertain light.

And sooth to say*, these latter years
30 Strange fancies now and then
Had filled his cell with scenes of life
And forms of living men.

Such wildering** scenes, such flitting shapes
As feverish dreams display:
35 What if those fancies still increase
And reason quite decay?

But hark***, what sounds have struck his ear;
Voices of men they seem;
And two have entered now his cell;
40 Can this too be a dream?

'Orlando, hear our joyful news:
Revenge and liberty!
Your foes are dead, and we are come
At last to set you free.'

45 So spoke the elder of the two,
And in the captive's eyes
He looked for gleaming ecstasy
But only found surprise.

'My foes are dead! It must be then
50 That all mankind are gone.
For they were all my deadly foes
And friends I had not one.'

Anne Brontë

* sooth to say — *truth be told*
** wildering — *confusing*
*** hark — *listen*

41

1. According to the poem, the prisoner was sat in a "dungeon deep" (line 1). This means:

   A   the dungeon is far underground.

   B   the dungeon is deep under the sea.

   C   the dungeon is heavily guarded.

   D   the dungeon has very high ceilings.

2. What is the prisoner doing between lines 1-20?

   A   Silently contemplating unknown thoughts while in a daze.

   B   Dreaming of a time when he may be released from the dungeon.

   C   Yearning to go somewhere where it is lighter.

   D   Happily reminiscing about things that happened in the past.

3. What reason does the narrator give for the prisoner losing "regret and hope" (line 11)?

   A   He has entirely forgotten about his life outside of the dungeon.

   B   He has been locked up by himself for a very long time.

   C   He has become fixated on spooky features of the dungeon.

   D   He realises that it is right that he is punished for his wrong-doings.

4. According to the poem, the prisoner no longer "sighs for freedom" (line 14). What does this mean?

   A   The prisoner no longer shouts to be set free.

   B   The prisoner doesn't mind that he is in the dungeon any more.

   C   The prisoner has given up longing to be released.

   D   The prisoner doesn't know when he might be released.

5. Which word best describes how the prisoner feels throughout the poem?

    A   Despondent

    B   Nostalgic

    C   Optimistic

    D   Agitated

6. What does the narrator describe as a "fitful flickering fire" (line 27)?

    A   The candles that used to burn in the dungeon.

    B   The prisoner's hope that all is not lost.

    C   The prisoner's grief when he was first imprisoned.

    D   The happiness of the prisoner's life before he was locked up.

7. What are the prisoner's "Strange fancies" (lines 30)?

    A   The words he speaks to himself.

    B   The pictures he draws.

    C   The things he hears outside his dungeon.

    D   The things he imagines.

8. The narrator asks, "What if those fancies still increase / And reason quite decay?" (lines 35-36). This means:

    A   the narrator wonders whether the prisoner will die in the dungeon.

    B   the narrator believes the fancies may become more rational.

    C   the narrator thinks the prisoner spends too long daydreaming.

    D   the narrator wonders whether the prisoner might eventually go mad.

TURN OVER ➡

9. What is happening in lines 37-40 of the poem?

   A   The prisoner is having a dream in which people enter his cell.

   B   The prisoner imagines that some men have entered the dungeon.

   C   Two people have come into the prisoner's cell.

   D   The prisoner hears the sounds of other prisoners in the dungeon.

10. Which of the following best describes how the "elder of the two" (line 45) expected the prisoner to respond?

   A   He expected him to be shocked at the news.

   B   He expected him to be relieved by the news.

   C   He expected him to be thankful at the prospect of being released.

   D   He expected him to be blissfully happy.

11. In the context of the poem, what does the word "rack" (line 16) mean?

   A   Trouble

   B   Panic

   C   Support

   D   Alarm

12. What does the word "flitting" (line 33) mean?

   A   Passing

   B   Darting

   C   Bolting

   D   Flowing

END OF TEST

/ 12

You have **10 minutes** to do this test. Work as quickly and as accurately as you can.

Read this passage carefully and answer the questions that follow.

Burning Rubber

The car flew into the air like a firework. Lilo hung tightly to her seat as the car rose, a feeling of weightlessness overcoming her limbs as she soared higher. After a brief pause, she felt the direction of movement change. She could see through the windscreen that the race track was hurtling towards her.

5   Moments later, the crunching of metal pierced Lilo's ears and the car shook awfully from side to side. Expecting the car to roll, she braced herself to be flung to one side, but the tyres gripped firmly to the tarmac. Though it felt like she had been flying for an age, it must have been a matter of seconds. The bumpers of the other race cars were still visible, heading down the final straight of the penultimate lap and disappearing

10 around the hair-pin bend.

    As the sound of the rattling car subsided, Lilo could hear gasps from the crowds. She turned to look out of the window to her right, which framed the view of her pit team running to her assistance. But Thunderbolt had other ideas. Beneath the scratched, battered bonnet, the engine started to purr stubbornly.

15   Returning fully to her senses, Lilo scanned the car's vitals via the onboard computer. Fortunately, none of her companion's internal functions were harmed, but she knew the chassis would not be in good shape.

    "Thunder?" she whispered into the dashboard. "I'm sorry, I just didn't see those rocks. I bet you Aaron planted them there. There was no way he'd have been able to overtake

20 me otherwise. We need to get you to the garage." She patted the steering wheel.

    At this last sentence, Thunderbolt let out a vigorous rev, his headlights glowing brightly and the dials on his dashboard spinning with defiance.

    Lilo smiled. "If you're sure you can take it," she said, admiring her old friend's determination. She slid the car into gear and jammed on the accelerator. Thunderbolt's

25 wheels started spinning and soon the cheering crowd and Lilo's perplexed pit team were hardly discernible in the rear-view mirror.

TURN OVER ➡

1. According to the text, the car flew into the air "like a firework" (line 1). This means:

    A   the car was thrown sideways by an explosion.

    B   there was a loud bang when the car flew off the track.

    C   the car soared into the air suddenly and violently.

    D   the car sparkled in the sunlight as it flew upwards.

2. According to the text, "the crunching of metal pierced Lilo's ears and the car shook awfully from side to side" (lines 5-6). What causes this?

    A   Lilo's car has been hit by falling rocks.

    B   Lilo's car has landed heavily on the race track.

    C   Lilo's car has been hit by another racing driver.

    D   Lilo's car has rolled off the race track.

3. Where and when does Lilo's crash occur?

    A   Near to the finishing line, on the second-to-last lap.

    B   On the edge of a tight corner on the second lap.

    C   In front of the grandstand, on the final lap.

    D   Near to the pit area, on the first lap.

4. What "other ideas" does Thunderbolt have in line 13?

    A   He wants to continue with the race.

    B   He thinks his engine needs seeing to, rather than his chassis.

    C   He wishes to retire from the race, rather than being fixed.

    D   He wants to drive himself to the garage, rather than being helped by the pit team.

5. Which of the following words best describes the appearance of Thunderbolt's chassis after the crash?

    A   Flimsy

    B   Crumbling

    C   Destroyed

X   D   Impaired

6. How does Lilo know that the car's interior is not harmed after the crash?

    A   She can hear the engine making a roaring noise.

    B   The car's computer is showing normal readings.

    C   The dials on the dashboard are spinning.

    D   The chassis has taken all of the impact.

7. What does Lilo believe caused her to crash?

    A   The uneven ground on the race track.

    B   The fact she wasn't concentrating on the track.

    C   Obstacles put in her way by another racing driver.

    D   Debris thrown onto the track by someone in the crowd.

8. According to the passage, Lilo "patted the steering wheel" (line 20). Why does she do this?

    A   She wishes to check if the steering was damaged.

    B   She needs to encourage Thunderbolt to continue racing.

    C   She wants to start driving Thunderbolt towards the garage.

    D   She wishes to reassure and show affection to Thunderbolt.

TURN OVER ➡

9. Thunderbolt is described as Lilo's "old friend" (line 23). What does this mean?

   A   Thunderbolt is a retired racing car.

   B   Thunderbolt is the oldest car Lilo has driven.

   C   Lilo has known Thunderbolt for a long time.

   D   Thunderbolt is Lilo's favourite car.

10. What is the most likely reason why Lilo's pit team are described as "perplexed" (line 25)?

   A   They don't expect Lilo and Thunderbolt to drive off after the crash.

   B   They don't know what caused Lilo to crash.

   C   They are unsure how best to fix the damage to Thunderbolt.

   D   They aren't sure why the crowd are cheering.

11. What does "subsided" (line 11) mean?

   A   Hushed

   B   Abated

   C   Disappeared

   D   Vacated

12. What does "discernible" (line 26) mean?

   A   Distinguishable

   B   Audible

   C   Tangible

   D   Measurable

END OF TEST

8 / 12

Time for a break! This puzzle is a great way to practise your **logic** skills.

Choral Chaos

Dale was hired to photograph the Greenstone choir. The photo turned out great, but he forgot to write down who was who. Use the clues below to work out who stood where. Write the correct name in the corresponding numbered box for each person.

1.
3. *Milo*
5. *Ruth*
2. *Linda*
4.
6.

7.
9.
11.
8.
10.
12.

Paul: "I'm wearing a blue tie."

Alfred: "I'm directly behind Nico."

Julie: "I'm stood between Nico and Adrian."

Ruth: "I'm not wearing a blue bow."

Leo: "I'm the third person along from Ian."

Ian: "I'm standing on the end of a row."

Adrian: "I am on the front row."

Peggy: "I'm not wearing a blue cardigan."

Nico: "I'm not wearing a jacket."

Linda: "I'm on the back row."

Ryan: "I'm stood next to Peggy."

Milo: "I'm stood two places along from Ruth."

You have **10 minutes** to do this test. Work as quickly and as accurately as you can.

Read this passage carefully and answer the questions that follow.

Exoplanets

More than 3,450 exoplanets, planets that orbit stars other than the Sun, have been officially identified in our galaxy. However, scientists believe our galaxy alone may contain trillions more, at least one for each star.

Though possible exoplanets were reported during the nineteenth century, many
5　scientists were unconvinced about their existence. It wasn't until 1995, when the 'wobble method' provided proof for the presence of the exoplanet 51 Pegasi b that the scientific community began to credit such reports and an international search for exoplanets began. During this search, scientists under Paul Butler and Geoff Marcy reassessed data they'd been accumulating for the previous few years and found
10　70 of the first 100 exoplanets to be identified. These exoplanets had initially gone unnoticed in their data as they showed characteristics that scientists at the time didn't think exoplanets could exhibit.

The hunt intensified in 2009 when NASA introduced the Kepler Space Telescope. Before it malfunctioned in 2013, Kepler detected more than 2,000 objects that
15　have been confirmed as exoplanets and 2,400 potential exoplanets. State-of-the-art instruments like the European CoRoT satellite, which functioned from 2006 to 2012, were also used to find new exoplanets. Kepler started gathering data again in 2014 using its remaining capabilities, and it has been in commission ever since.

Today, scientists are focussing on discovering terrestrial exoplanets, Earth-like
20　planets which primarily consist of rocks and metals. If these planets are in the habitable zone of their star, they could hold water, a prerequisite for life on Earth. To date, there are 352 confirmed terrestrial exoplanets, at least six of which are similar to Earth and within habitable zones. In 2016, the closest terrestrial exoplanet yet, Proxima Centauri b, was confirmed by data acquired from the ESO 3.6 m Telescope
25　and the Very Large Telescope. Despite sitting in a habitable zone, life may not be possible on this planet due its proximity to its host star, so the search for other habitable worlds and extraterrestrial life continues.

Answer these questions about the text that you've just read.
Circle the letter that matches the correct answer.

1. Why could the number of exoplanets in our galaxy be described as 'innumerable'?

   A   Over 3,000 exoplanets have already been discovered.

   B   Scientists think that there may be more exoplanets than stars.

   C   It is suspected that a huge number of exoplanets exist in our galaxy.

   D   It is hard to officially confirm the existence of an exoplanet.

2. Which of the following best describes scientists' opinions of exoplanets during the nineteenth century?

   A   Sceptical

   B   Indecisive

   C   Apprehensive

   D   Assured

3. According to the text, what happened immediately after the discovery of 51 Pegasi b?

   A   International groups launched missions to explore new exoplanets.

   B   Plans were made to inhabit 51 Pegasi b.

   C   Astronomers from across the globe began to look for exoplanets.

   D   Several countries claimed that their scientists had found more exoplanets.

4. According to the text, Butler and Marcy identified exoplanets that "had initially gone unnoticed in their data" (lines 10-11). This tells us that Butler and Marcy:

   A   were the first to confirm the existence of exoplanets.

   B   already had data showing signs of exoplanets in 1995.

   C   didn't properly examine their data when they first gathered it.

   D   kept the fact that they had identified exoplanets a secret for a few years.

TURN OVER ➡

5. The CoRoT satellite is described as being "state-of-the-art" (line 15). This means:

   A   it was designed using the latest technology.

   B   it has been built to be visually striking.

   C   the techniques used to build it have been practised for many years.

   D   it is continually updated with new, modern features.

6. The Kepler Space Telescope is described as being "in commission" (line 18). This means that:

   A   it is being redesigned.

   B   it is in service.

   C   it is in need of repair.

   D   it is under construction.

7. Why have scientists become more focussed on finding terrestrial planets in habitable zones?

   A   They could be used to supplement Earth's water supply.

   B   They could support other life forms.

   C   They are rich with metals that could be mined.

   D   They are likely to have similar dimensions to Earth.

8. Which of the following was not in use in 2016?

   A   The Kepler Space Telescope

   B   The CoRoT satellite

   C   The ESO 3.6 m Telescope

   D   The Very Large Telescope

9. Which of the following statements about Proxima Centauri b must be true?

   A   It is the most Earth-like exoplanet discovered so far.

   B   Scientists have confirmed that it can support life.

   C   Traces of water could exist on its surface.

   D   It is one of only six terrestrial exoplanets to have been discovered.

10. Which of the following is not mentioned in the text?

   A   The continent which is responsible for the CoRoT satellite.

   B   The name of a technique used to prove the presence of exoplanets.

   C   The organisation responsible for launching the Kepler Space Telescope.

   D   The distance between Earth and the closest exoplanet yet discovered.

11. What does "characteristics" (line 11) mean?

   A   Properties

   B   Talents

   C   Personalities

   D   Distinctions

12. What does "intensified" (line 13) mean?

   A   Accrued

   B   Soared

   C   Escalated

   D   Emphasised

END OF TEST

/ 12

You have **10 minutes** to do this test. Work as quickly and as accurately as you can.

Read this poem carefully and answer the questions that follow.

An abridged extract from 'The Discoverer of the North Cape'

Othere, the old sea-captain,
  Who dwelt in Helgoland,
To King Alfred, the Lover of Truth,
Brought a snow-white walrus-tooth,
5   Which he held in his brown right hand.

His figure was tall and stately,
  Like a boy's his eye appeared;
His hair was yellow as hay,
But threads of a silvery gray
10   Gleamed in his tawny beard.

Hearty and hale was Othere,
  His cheek had the colour of oak;
With a kind of laugh in his speech,
Like the sea-tide on a beach,
15   As unto the King he spoke.

And Alfred, King of the Saxons,
  Had a book upon his knees,
And wrote down the wondrous tale
Of him who was first to sail
20   Into the Arctic seas.

"So far I live to the northward,
  No man lives north of me;
To the east are wild mountain-chains;
And beyond them meres* and plains;
25   To the westward all is sea.

"I ploughed the land with horses,
  But my heart was ill at ease,
For the old seafaring men
Came to me now and then,
30   With their sagas of the seas;--

"Of Iceland and of Greenland,
  And the stormy Hebrides,
And the undiscovered deep;--
Oh I could not eat nor sleep
35   For thinking of those seas.

"To the northward stretched the desert,
  How far I fain** would know;
So at last I sallied forth***,
And three days sailed due north,
40   As far as the whale-ships go.

"The days grew longer and longer,
  Till they became as one,
And northward through the haze
I saw the sullen blaze
45   Of the red midnight sun.

"And then uprose before me,
  Upon the water's edge,
The huge and haggard shape
Of that unknown North Cape,
50   Whose form is like a wedge.

* meres — *lakes*   **fain — *gladly*   ***sallied forth — *set off*   **Henry W. Longfellow**

1. Which of the following best describes the appearance of Othere?

    A   Pale and lanky

    B   Stout and youthful

    C   Imposing and dignified

    D   Decrepit and hunched

2. Which of the following best describes Othere's voice?

    A   Affable

    B   Sombre

    C   Weary

    D   Rasping

3. Which statement best describes the intention of Alfred in the poem?

    A   To tell Othere a story about a famous sea voyage.

    B   To challenge Othere's version of events.

    C   To document the details of how Othere discovered the North Cape.

    D   To reward Othere with a walrus tooth.

4. Which of the following statements best describes the location of Othere's home?

    A   On a plain by a lake.

    B   By the coast, with a view of a large mountain range.

    C   Due south of another settlement.

    D   Next to a lake at the foot of a mountain.

TURN OVER ➡

5. According to the poem, which of the following is not a reason why Othere decided to sail northwards?

   A   He wanted to find out how far north the seas stretched.

   B   He was obsessed by the idea of exploring uncharted waters.

   C   He had grown restless with his life on the land.

   D   He wished to see whether seas described by other mariners really existed.

6. Which of the following statements about Othere must be false?

   A   He has been a voyager all his life.

   B   He is an old acquaintance of Alfred.

   C   He has led a relatively reclusive life.

   D   He wishes to be remembered as a great captain.

7. According to the poem, which of the following must be true?

   A   The whale-ships often sail to the east of Helgoland.

   B   The whale-ships journey north from Helgoland.

   C   The whale-ships only sail during daylight.

   D   The whale-ships frequently explore seas around Greenland and Iceland.

8. What happens as Othere's voyage continues?

   A   The nights draw in.

   B   The weather gets hotter.

   C   The sun ceases to set.

   D   The moon becomes brighter.

9. According to the poem, which of the following words does not describe the North Cape?

    A   Unexplored

    B   Towering

    C   Weather-beaten

    D   Graceful

10. Which of the following is not mentioned in the poem?

    A   The place where Othere lives.

    B   The name of the people that Alfred rules.

    C   The waters where the North Cape is located.

    D   The type of boat on which Othere sailed to the North Cape.

11. What does "Hearty and hale" (line 11) mean?

    A   Passionate and dedicated

    B   Strong and healthy

    C   Impatient and restless

    D   Eager and hopeful

12. What does "sagas" (line 30) mean?

    A   Tales

    B   Catalogues

    C   Versions

    D   Rumours

END OF TEST

/ 12

You have **10 minutes** to do this test. Work as quickly and as accurately as you can.

Read this passage carefully and answer the questions that follow.

An abridged extract from 'Cranford'

Cranford is in possession of the Amazons*; all the holders of houses above a certain rent are women. If a couple come to settle in the town, the gentleman disappears; he is either fairly frightened to death by being the only man in the Cranford evening parties, or he is accounted for by being with his regiment, his ship, or closely engaged
5 in business in the great neighbouring town of Drumble, distant only twenty miles on a railroad. In short, whatever does become of the gentlemen, they are not at Cranford.

The Cranford ladies have only an occasional little quarrel, spirited out in a few peppery words; just enough to prevent the even tenor of their lives from becoming too flat. Their dress is very independent of fashion; as they observe, "What does it signify
10 how we dress here at Cranford, where everybody knows us?" And if they go from home, "What does it signify how we dress here, where nobody knows us?"

Then there were rules and regulations for visiting and calls; and they were announced to any young people who might be staying in the town.

"Our friends have sent to inquire how you are after your journey, my dear" (fifteen
15 miles in a carriage); "they will give you some rest to-morrow, but the next day they will call; so be at liberty after twelve — from twelve to three are our calling hours."

Then, after they had called—

"It is the third day; I dare say your mamma has told you never to let more than three days elapse between receiving a call and returning it; and also, that you are never to
20 stay longer than a quarter of an hour."

"But am I to look at my watch? How am I to find out when a quarter of an hour has passed?"

"You must keep thinking about the time, my dear, and not allow yourself to forget it in conversation."

25 As everybody had this rule in their minds, of course no absorbing subject was ever spoken about.

Elizabeth Gaskell

* Amazons — *powerful women*

Answer these questions about the text that you've just read.
Circle the letter that matches the correct answer.

1. According to the text, "all the holders of houses above a certain rent are women" (lines 1-2). What does this suggest about Cranford?

    A   In Cranford, women pay less rent than the men.

    B   Only women are allowed to be tenants in Cranford.

    C   Many of the richest people in Cranford are women.

    D   All women in Cranford own houses.

2. Which of the following is not given as a reason in the passage for why the men of Cranford are absent?

    A   They are away on military service.

    B   They are busy working in a different town.

    C   They are at sea.

    D   They marry in Drumble and then move away.

3. Which of the following statements must be true about Cranford?

    A   Cranford is bigger than Drumble.

    B   Cranford can only be reached by road.

    C   There is a another town within twenty-one miles of Cranford.

    D   There is a regimental base near Cranford.

4. Which of the following statements is true about the ladies of Cranford?

    A   They tend to resolve any disagreements quite quickly.

    B   They think it is important to keep up with the latest trends.

    C   They are always cordial towards one another.

    D   They avoid people who come from outside of Cranford.

TURN OVER ➡

5. The lives of the ladies of Cranford are described as having an "even tenor" (line 8). This means the ladies of Cranford:

    A   are all of the same rank and status.

    B   live relatively settled lives.

    C   lead quite boring lives.

    D   have a comfortable income.

6. Which of the following best describes how the ladies of Cranford dress?

    A   The clothes they wear depend on the place they are visiting.

    B   They don't allow their fashion to be affected by the opinions of others.

    C   They follow the fashion trends that are popular outside of Cranford.

    D   They dress plainly so as to remain anonymous.

7. According to the text, ladies of Cranford are advised that they should "be at liberty after twelve" (line 16). This means that they should:

    A   make sure they are free to do chores at twelve.

    B   not be inside their house after twelve.

    C   spend the morning doing things so that they are not busy after twelve.

    D   only take time for themselves if it is past twelve.

8. According to the text, when would it be socially unacceptable to return a call?

    A   At quarter-past-three, three days after receiving a call.

    B   At two-thirty in the afternoon the following day.

    C   Around 48 hours after a call has been received.

    D   At noon the next day.

9. How do people in Cranford keep track of the time during a social call?

    A   They frequently check their watches.

    B   They rely on their host to inform them what the time is.

    C   They frequently mention the time during the conversation.

    D   They remain unengaged in conversation.

10. According to the text, what is the effect of Cranford's rules about calls?

    A   It gives everyone time to visit all of their friends during calling hours.

    B   It means that people have to visit each other more regularly.

    C   It stops people from getting bored while making calls.

    D   It limits what topics can be discussed during a visit.

11. What does "regulations" (line 12) mean?

    A   Authorities

    B   Penalties

    C   Guidelines

    D   Adjustments

12. In the context of the extract, what does "absorbing" (line 25) mean?

    A   Captivating

    B   Assimilating

    C   Appropriate

    D   Advantageous

END OF TEST

/ 12

Time for a break! These puzzles are a great way to practise your **vocabulary** skills.

Target Practice

Fill in the missing letters on the target so that each section spells a word that means the same, or the nearly the same, as the word in bold. One has been done for you.

The letters in the target's innermost circle can be rearranged to make a word that means 'with kindness'.

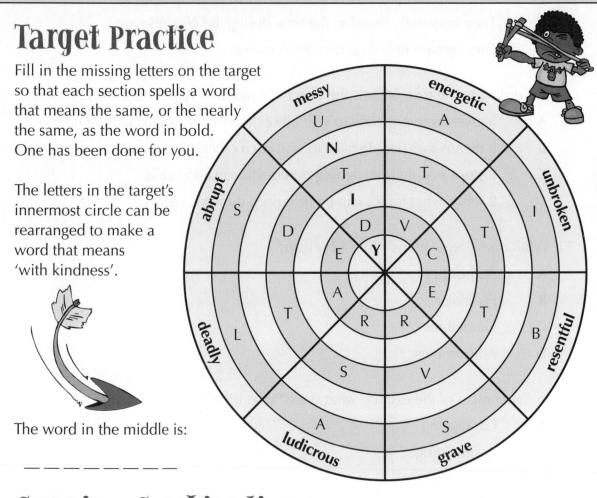

The word in the middle is:

_ _ _ _ _ _ _ _

Cunning Combinations

For each pair of words, add the letters of the right-hand word to the left-hand word to make a new word. The letters from the right-hand word can go anywhere and don't have to stay together, but they must stay in the same order. The first one has been done.

REAL — TIED	STAIN — RING	PAT — SURE
R E T A I L E D	_ _ _ _ _ _ _ _	_ _ _ _ _ _ _
HEAT — SITE	TAP — RISING	SLY — IMP
_ _ _ _ _ _ _ _	_ _ _ _ _ _ _ _ _	_ _ _ _ _ _

You have **10 minutes** to do this test. Work as quickly and as accurately as you can.

Read this passage carefully and answer the questions that follow.

The Journey

First awoke dawn's choir. The sparrows, chaffinches and other occupants of the hedgerows shattered the quiet with their anthems. Then, the radiant sun surfaced above the lush fields, encasing the dew-soaked grass in liquid gold.

As the light of the dawn stirred the inhabitants of the rural scene, so the blinding
5 rays woke Tim. He opened his eyes slowly and became suddenly aware that he was not waking where he expected. Shooting to his feet, Tim found himself standing on the crest of a hill that commanded a fine view over the surrounding landscape. The scene was spectacular, boasting uncultivated heath, meadows peppered with sheep, expansive corn fields and lush meadows that were slowly browning, ready for the
10 hay harvest. But not one familiar sight could Tim identify. The sounds, too, were unknown — he could hear the loud flow of water from a nearby river. He must be a long way from home, where the only noise he could ever hear was the steady drone from below his tower block of people caught in gridlock.

Tim tried to conjure up details of the previous evening and how he had come to
15 this alien place, but the memories slipped through his head like water. Suddenly, from behind him came a small, high-pitched voice.

"What-cha doing?" it said.

Tim wheeled around but couldn't see anything. He scanned the area in front of him before following the sound of tiny feet down towards the grass. His mouth fell open.
20 "Oi!" said the tiny animal as Tim took in the furry speaker. "It's rude to stare!" It bounced so high that for a moment it was looking at Tim square in the eyes.

"But how?" cried Tim. "How are you talking? You're not meant to be able to talk!"

"Well, if I'm not meant to be able to talk," replied the small grey figure, "I suppose you won't want me to tell you where you are." It twitched its whiskers indignantly and
25 jumped off through the grass, its cotton tail like a white beacon in a sea of green.

"No! Wait!" cried Tim, racing after the creature vigorously.

TURN OVER ➡

Answer these questions about the text that you've just read.
Circle the letter that matches the correct answer.

1. According to the passage, what caused Tim to wake up?

   A   The loud bird song

   B   The cold dew

   C   The bright sunrise

   D   The rustling of birds in the hedgerows

2. According to the text, the hill "commanded a fine view over the surrounding landscape" (line 7). This means that:

   A   Tim has a picturesque view of a large hill.

   B   the hill gives Tim a particularly good vantage point over the area.

   C   being on top of the hill makes Tim feel incredibly powerful.

   D   the view from the top of the hill shows the landscape in incredible detail.

3. Which of the following landscapes is not mentioned in the text?

   A   Wild moorland

   B   Fields of crops

   C   Fields of hay bales

   D   Pastoral farmland

4. What does the "steady drone" (line 12) describe?

   A   The sound of trains on the tracks.

   B   The sound of traffic on the roads.

   C   The sound of people talking.

   D   The sound of aeroplanes.

5. Which of the following best describes where Tim lives?

   A   A rural village

   B   A grand mansion

   C   A city

   D   A riverside town

6. According to the passage, Tim's memories of the previous evening "slipped through his head like water" (line 15). This means:

   A   the memories were chilling.

   B   the memories were easy to recall.

   C   the memories flowed clearly into one other.

   D   the memories were forgotten as quickly as they were remembered.

7. According to the text, after Tim first saw the creature, his "mouth fell open" (line 19). Why did this happen?

   A   Tim was shocked by what he saw.

   B   Tim was preparing to shout at the creature.

   C   Tim was screaming loudly, as he was startled by the creature.

   D   Tim was beginning to smile.

8. What does Tim think is the strangest feature of the animal?

   A   Its small size.

   B   Its ability to talk.

   C   Its ability to become invisible.

   D   Its ability to bounce very high.

TURN OVER ➡

9. What was the creature that addressed Tim?

   A   A fox

   B   A mouse

   C   A rabbit

   D   There is no evidence in the passage to suggest what animal it was.

10. Why does Tim run off after the creature at the end of the passage?

   A   He wishes to learn more about the creature.

   B   He realises the creature may be able to help him.

   C   He doesn't know how to get down from the top of the hill.

   D   He knows that if he follows the creature it will lead him home.

11. What does "indignantly" (line 24) mean?

   A   Bitterly

   B   Firmly

   C   Wistfully

   D   Recklessly

12. What does "vigorously" (line 26) mean?

   A   Angrily

   B   Energetically

   C   Impatiently

   D   Forlornly

END OF TEST

/ 12

You have **10 minutes** to do this test. Work as quickly and as accurately as you can.

Read this passage carefully and answer the questions that follow.

The Terracotta Army

In 1974, a group of farmers set out to build a well to the north-east of the city of Xi'an, in the Shaanxi Province of China. After they unearthed pieces of a pottery figure, Chinese archaeologists came to investigate. What they found was one of the great ancient wonders of the world which had lain undiscovered for just under 2,200

5 years: burial pits containing thousands of pottery warriors.

This Terracotta Army was built to guard and serve the great Chinese king and emperor, Qin Shi Huang, in the afterlife. It is estimated that there are around 8,000 terracotta figures in the burial pits. So far, around 2,000 of these figures, which include foot soldiers, standing archers and chariots, complete with their drivers and

10 horses, have been excavated.

Though the size of the army is impressive, the detail of each figure makes the collection truly breathtaking. Every soldier stands at human height and each one has a unique expression and facial features. There would have been even greater variations between the soldiers than there are now, as each figure was initially

15 hand-painted with bright colours. Each figure was also originally armed with real weapons made of bronze. Miraculously, archaeologists found that many of these weapons were still sharp.

The pits containing the Terracotta Army are just one part of the huge mausoleum of Qin Shi Huang. The process of constructing the site began when the king assumed

20 the throne at the age of 13 and, although seemingly unfinished, it was sealed after the king's death around 40 years later. The main tomb, which lies to the west of the Terracotta Army pits, remains unexplored, though historical writings give us clues about what it may be like. One report details a great complex featuring rivers of mercury (a liquid that Qin Shi Huang may have believed was the elixir of life, but we

25 now know to be toxic). There are people opposed to beginning excavation work on this site, because they believe that the technology does not currently exist to unearth the treasures without damaging them.

TURN OVER ➡

Answer these questions about the text that you've just read.
Circle the letter that matches the correct answer.

1. Where was the Terracotta Army discovered?

   A   On the borders of the Xi'an district, a province of China.

   B   Near Xi'an, in the far north-east of China.

   C   In the Shaanxi Province of China, to the north-east of Xi'an.

   D   To the north-east of the Shaanxi Province of China, near Xi'an.

2. Who first discovered traces of the Terracotta Army in 1974?

   A   Farmers who were digging to plant crops.

   B   People who were searching for pottery.

   C   Chinese archaeologists who were excavating.

   D   People who were boring for water.

3. Which of the following best describes the Terracotta Army?

   A   A tribute to an army that fought in China over 2000 years ago.

   B   A ceremonial army built to protect Qin Shi Huang in the next life.

   C   A decorative army built solely to adorn the tomb of Qin Shi Huang.

   D   A defensive army to prevent attacks from looters.

4. According to the text, which of the following figures do not feature in the terracotta army?

   A   Charioteers

   B   Infantry

   C   Mounted archers

   D   Bowmen

5. Which of the following could not be used to describe the terracotta soldiers?

   A   Intricate

   B   Man-sized

   C   Generic

   D   Realistic

6. Which of the following statements must be false?

   A   Much of the paint on the terracotta warriors that have been excavated is still intact.

   B   Some of the terracotta figures have been irreparably damaged.

   C   The Terracotta Army is spread over multiple chambers.

   D   The Terracotta Army features both humans and animals.

7. When did the building of the tomb of Qin Shi Huang begin?

   A   40 years after the death of Qin Shi Huang.

   B   When Qin Shi Huang was 40 years old.

   C   In the year 2200 BC.

   D   When the reign of Qin Shi Huang began.

8. According to the text, which of the following statements must be false?

   A   Further terracotta figures are expected to be found in the main tomb.

   B   Construction of the burial site was finished during Qin Shi Huang's lifetime.

   C   Excavations at the site started in the late 20th century.

   D   The Terracotta Army pits lie to the east of the main tomb of Qin Shi Huang.

TURN OVER ➡

Test 16

9. What is the most likely reason for the supposed presence of "rivers of mercury" (lines 23-24) in the main tomb?

    A   Builders thought the presence of poisonous metals would deter looters.

    B   The rivers of mercury separated the different chambers of the tomb.

    C   Builders thought mercury rivers would endure better than rivers of water.

    D   People at the time believed that mercury may have had special life-giving powers.

10. According to the text, what is the likely future of the main tomb of Qin Shi Huang?

    A   It will be excavated when enough funds have been raised to do so.

    B   It is unlikely to ever be excavated due to high levels of poisonous metals.

    C   It will be explored when archaeological techniques have developed.

    D   The tomb will collapse, destroying its contents.

11. What does "excavated" (line 10) mean?

    A   Uncovered

    B   Analysed

    C   Identified

    D   Surveyed

12. What does "miraculously" (line 16) mean?

    A   Disturbingly

    B   Remarkably

    C   Shockingly

    D   Curiously

END OF TEST

/ 12

You have **10 minutes** to do this test. Work as quickly and as accurately as you can.

Read this passage carefully and answer the questions that follow.

An extract from 'Far from the Madding Crowd'

When Farmer Oak smiled, the corners of his mouth spread till they were within an unimportant distance of his ears, his eyes were reduced to chinks, and diverging wrinkles appeared round them, extending upon his countenance like the rays in a rudimentary sketch of the rising sun.

5   His Christian name was Gabriel, and on working days he was a young man of sound judgment, easy motions, proper dress, and general good character. On Sundays he was a man of misty views, rather given to postponing, and hampered by his best clothes and umbrella: upon the whole, one who felt himself to occupy morally that vast middle space of Laodicean* neutrality which lay between the Communion people** of the parish and

10 the drunken section, — that is, he went to church, but yawned privately by the time the congregation reached the Nicene creed***, and thought of what there would be for dinner when he meant to be listening to the sermon. Or, to state his character as it stood in the scale of public opinion, when his friends and critics were in tantrums, he was considered rather a bad man; when they were pleased, he was rather a good man; when they were

15 neither, he was a man whose moral colour was a kind of pepper-and-salt mixture.

     Since he lived six times as many working-days as Sundays, Oak's appearance in his old clothes was most peculiarly his own — the mental picture formed by his neighbours in imagining him being always dressed in that way. He wore a low-crowned felt hat, spread out at the base by tight jamming upon the head for security in high winds, and a coat like

20 Dr. Johnson's****; his lower extremities being encased in ordinary leather leggings and boots emphatically large, affording to each foot a roomy apartment so constructed that any wearer might stand in a river all day long and know nothing of damp.

Thomas Hardy

* Laodicean — *indifferent*   ** Communion people — *devout people*
*** Nicene creed — *a passage common in Christian church services*
**** Dr Johnson — *an English writer who was known to wear a large coat*

TURN OVER ➡

              Test 17

Answer these questions about the text that you've just read.
Circle the letter that matches the correct answer.

1. Which of the following are not features of Oak's face when he smiles?

   A   An extremely broad grin

   B   Dimples in his cheeks

   C   Narrow eyes

   D   Lines around his eyes

2. What is Oak's full name?

   A   Farmer Oak

   B   Farmer Oak Gabriel

   C   Oak Gabriel

   D   Gabriel Oak

3. How would Oak describe himself?

   A   Devout

   B   A drunkard

   C   Someone with a half-hearted attitude to religion

   D   Someone who opposes religion

4. According to the text, Oak "thought of what there would be for dinner when he meant to be listening to the sermon" (lines 11-12). This means:

   A   Oak's mind wandered during sermons.

   B   Oak was familiar with the sermons so did not need to listen to them fully.

   C   Oak didn't have time for breakfast before church.

   D   Oak was reminded of dinner by what he heard during the sermons.

5. Which of the following statements is true?
   - **A**   Oak suits his best clothes more than his working clothes.
   - **B**   Oak does not feel at ease when wearing his best clothes.
   - **C**   Oak carries an umbrella with him throughout the week.
   - **D**   Oak wears his working clothes to church.

6. Which of the following best describes people's opinions of Oak?
   - **A**   They only think fondly of him when they are indebted to him.
   - **B**   Their opinions of him are fickle.
   - **C**   They think he is mostly a bad man.
   - **D**   They think he is very argumentative.

7. According to the text, people sometimes saw Oak as "a man whose moral colour was a kind of pepper-and-salt mixture" (line 15). This means:
   - **A**   they thought there were good and bad qualities to Oak's character.
   - **B**   they thought Oak's morals were often dubious.
   - **C**   they thought it was often unclear how Oak might react to a situation.
   - **D**   they were irritated by Oak's morals.

8. According to the text, when does Oak wear his best clothes?
   - **A**   On Saturdays and Sundays
   - **B**   Six times a week
   - **C**   On Sundays only
   - **D**   Six times a month

TURN OVER ➡

9. Which of the following clothes does Oak wear for work?

    1.   His best clothes

    2.   A cloth hat

    3.   Distinctive, brown leggings

    4.   A coat that belongs to Dr. Johnson

    A   1 and 2

    B   2 only

    C   2 and 3

    D   3 and 4

10. Which of the following statements best describes Oak's boots?

    A   Fashionable and well made

    B   Tight-fitting and waterproof

    C   Moth-eaten and roomy

    D   Spacious and robust

11. What does "countenance" (line 3) mean?

    A   Appearance

    B   Attitude

    C   Semblance

    D   Personality

12. What does "postponing" (line 7) mean?

    A   Cancelling

    B   Delaying

    C   Terminating

    D   Impeding

END OF TEST

/ 12

Time for a break! This puzzle is a great way to practise your **word-making** skills.

Puzzle Paws

Fit the puzzle pieces into the square grids below, so that each row spells out the name of an animal. If you fill in the grid correctly, then you'll also find the name of an extra animal running down the blue diagonal line. One piece has already been placed into each grid.

You have **10 minutes** to do this test. Work as quickly and as accurately as you can.

Read this passage carefully and answer the questions that follow.

Mars Space Log of Ahmed Chaudry

14:00, 231 sols since landing. We awoke to a terrible dust storm this morning so remained inside the base for four hours until it subsided. That was frustrating, as it meant we'd wasted a lot of the sol (that's the word we use to mean a Mars day) confined in the camp and unable to continue with our work. Mars has a beautiful
5 landscape but a violent temper too.

Yestersol*, we returned from our mission up north in the Tharsis region. This is a volcanic area on the planet's equator. The volcanoes are extinct, but they have left behind arid deserts and a confusing maze of canyons. We had to quickly take cover every time a gust rushed through the canyon or a small dust storm flared up. But
10 standing on the area's second highest mountain and volcano, Ascraeus Mons, we saw that the area was majestic. We didn't climb all the way, of course: at 18 kilometres high, it would have taken us far too long, and we have more important work to do.

Today, Julia and Kofi analysed the atmospheric samples we took from the Tharsis region. As soon as the storm died down, I had to go outside for an hour to attend
15 to the robots, my area of expertise, before returning to the base. I then recorded a birthday message to my son, Mustafa, who turns eight tomorrow. I find it difficult to keep track of Earth days. There are 669 sols in a Mars year, which is the equivalent of 687 Earth days. It took a long time to get used to this system, which is very unlike Earth where there are 365 Earth days in a year. Thankfully, it's still the Earth year
20 2073 for another two Earth weeks, so that's easy to remember for the time being.

Tomorrow, we depart for Mars's south pole, where frozen carbon dioxide has formed cliffs of dry ice. Some time after that, we will go back to the region we returned from yestersol to investigate another volcano, Olympus Mons, which at 25 kilometres is the tallest mountain in the solar system. I'm glad we're having more adventures — the
25 'wake up at 7:00, sleep at 21:00' routine at the base is so monotonous.

* Yestersol — *the Mars day before today*

Answer these questions about the text that you've just read.
Circle the letter that matches the correct answer.

1. The weather in the Tharsis region is:

    A   so cold that there are cliffs of dry ice.

    B   constantly windy and overcast.

    C   wet and stormy.

    D   dry but sometimes very windy.

2. How many more sols will it be before Ahmed has spent a full Mars year on the planet?

    A   31

    B   134

    C   438

    D   456

3. Which of the following statements is false?

    A   Ascraeus Mons is an active volcano.

    B   The lower slopes of Ascraeus Mons are easily accessible.

    C   Ahmed believes it is easy to get lost in the Tharsis region's canyons.

    D   Ahmed thinks the Tharsis region's landscape is beautiful.

4. What was the primary aim of the mission to the Tharsis region?

    A   To collect atmospheric samples.

    B   To explore the deserts and canyons.

    C   To climb Ascraeus Mons.

    D   To assess the landscape.

TURN OVER ➡

5. At what time did Ahmed return to the base after fixing the robots?

   A   8:00

   B   11:00

   C   12:00

   D   14:00

6. In what Earth year was Ahmed's son born?

   A   2061

   B   2065

   C   2069

   D   2073

7. Which of the following statements is false?

   A   A day on Mars is longer than a day on Earth.

   B   Ahmed's son was born in January.

   C   Ahmed's son's birthday is on the 232nd sol of Ahmed's landing on Mars.

   D   Ahmed wrote a space log the sol before his son's birthday.

8. Which of the following statements must be true?

   1.   Including Ahmed, there are three people in the team.

   2.   Ahmed's base is located in Mars's southern hemisphere.

   3.   When at the base, the team is meant to go to bed at the same time every night.

   4.   The team's robots are always breaking and needing repairs.

   A   1 and 2

   B   1 and 3

   C   2 and 3

   D   2 and 4

9. Which of the following is true about Ahmed Chaudry?

    A   He enjoys the challenges presented by Mars's dust storms.

    B   He found that adapting to the time differences between Mars and Earth was a slow process.

    C   He has a teenage son.

    D   He likely joined the team because of his ability to analyse atmospheric samples.

10. Which of the following statements must be true?

    A   Olympus Mons is located in the Tharsis region.

    B   Olympus Mons is the second highest mountain on Mars.

    C   Olympus Mons is not volcanic.

    D   It would take almost twice as long to climb Olympus Mons as it would to climb Ascraeus Mons.

11. Which of the following is not mentioned in the text?

    A   The name of Ahmed's son.

    B   How long Ahmed's team have been on Mars.

    C   The time Ahmed wrote his log.

    D   How long the mission to the Tharsis region lasted.

12. Why does Ahmed dislike spending days at the base?

    A   He doesn't enjoy waking up early.

    B   He prefers his days to be less predictable.

    C   He associates staying inside the base with bad weather outside.

    D   He hates feeling compelled to look after the robots.

END OF TEST

/ 12

Test 19

You have **10 minutes** to do this test. Work as quickly and as accurately as you can.

> Read this passage carefully and answer the questions that follow.

Lascaux Cave Paintings

In 1940, four teenagers — Marcel Ravidat, Jacques Marsal, Georges Agnel and Simon Coencas — were walking Ravidat's dog, Robot, in the countryside around the village of Montignac, when they came across a small entrance to a cave. Montignac (in the Dordogne region of France) is said to have treasures hidden in
5 a cave nearby, so the boys went inside to investigate. Instead of treasure, they discovered huge prehistoric paintings, that date from around 19,000 years ago. The boys told one of their teachers, a member of the local prehistory society, and took him to see the paintings.

The paintings' humble discovery belies their significance. There are over
10 600 paintings and 1500 engravings in total which are spread across several chambers. The paintings mainly consist of horses, deer and aurochs (predecessors of cattle). Perhaps the most famous painting is the Great Black Bull, which at over five metres long is the largest cave painting animal yet discovered. Nearby, in a narrow part of the cave, sits the Chamber of Felines. This chamber's paintings — which
15 are unique amongst the others in the cave for including large cats — are more faded here than elsewhere. The only human depicted in the cave's paintings is a bird-headed man, who may represent a doctor or priest. Crucially, the paintings provide archaeologists with an insight into prehistoric lifestyles and beliefs.

After the discovery, the number of visitors to the cave (which was named
20 Lascaux) grew. As a result, guided tours of the cave began in 1948 — the paintings captivated tourists as they had their discoverers. Two of the teenagers who found the paintings, Ravidat and Marsal, became tour guides. However, the caves were closed to the public in 1963 when scientists discovered that the moisture from visitors' breath was contributing towards the paint fading. Replicas of the paintings
25 were made which tourists can visit instead. There are still concerns, as fungi has begun to take over the cave. Scientists are trying to remove the fungi in the hope of preserving the paintings for future generations.

Answer these questions about the text that you've just read.
Circle the letter that matches the correct answer.

1. According to the text, when did the teenagers find the cave?
   A   While they were looking for treasure in rural areas.
   B   While they were looking for cave paintings.
   C   While they were walking a dog in the countryside.
   D   While they were on a school trip with their teacher.

2. Where are the paintings located?
   A   In Montignac cave near the town of Dordogne.
   B   In Lascaux cave near the village of Montignac.
   C   In Montignac cave in the region of Dordogne.
   D   In Lascaux cave in the region of Montignac

3. According to the text, why are the cave paintings important?
   A   They reveal what extinct cattle looked like.
   B   They confirm the existence of large bulls in prehistoric France.
   C   They give visitors a glimpse into the practices of prehistoric doctors.
   D   They provide information about prehistoric life and religion.

4. Which of the following is the most likely reason why one part of the cave is called the Chamber of Felines?
   A   It is close to the image of the Great Black Bull.
   B   It includes images of cats on its walls.
   C   It includes paintings that are more faded than those in the rest of the cave.
   D   It is the part of the cave that Robot was most interested in.

TURN OVER ➡

5. Which of the following details is not included in the passage?

   A   The size of the painting of the Great Black Bull.

   B   Which animals are depicted in most of the paintings.

   C   The total number of engravings in the caves.

   D   The number of tour guides who worked at the cave during the 1950s.

6. Which of the following best describes the cave paintings?

   A   Extensive

   B   Medieval

   C   Invisible

   D   Fabricated

7. Which of the following is the most likely explanation for why people became aware of the boys' discovery?

   A   The boys sold the paintings to a museum.

   B   The cave paintings were so large that it became difficult to hide them.

   C   Other people stumbled across the paintings.

   D   The teenagers' teacher understood the significance of the paintings and so told others about them.

8. Why do you think Ravidat and Marsal became tour guides?

   A   They were enchanted by and committed to the paintings.

   B   They were told to do so by their teacher.

   C   They thought they would do a better job than anyone else.

   D   They were still hopeful of finding treasure in the caves.

9. Why were replicas made of the cave paintings?

    A   So that people will remember what they looked like if the originals fade.

    B   So tourists can enjoy seeing the paintings without causing them harm.

    C   Rockfalls in the caves made the originals inaccessible.

    D   Fungi had begun to destroy the original paintings.

10. Which of the following can be inferred from the passage?

    A   Ravidat and Marsal became rich and famous as a result of their discovery.

    B   The Great Black Bull was at the centre of prehistoric religious beliefs.

    C   The teenagers' discovery ultimately led to the paintings' deterioration.

    D   At the moment, nobody is allowed to enter the Lascaux cave.

11. What does "belies" (line 9) mean?

    A   Magnifies

    B   Denies

    C   Indicates

    D   Conceals

12. What does "depicted" (line 16) mean?

    A   Portrayed

    B   Unveiled

    C   Scribbled

    D   Transpired

END OF TEST

/ 12

Test 20

You have **10 minutes** to do this test. Work as quickly and as accurately as you can.

Read this poem carefully and answer the questions that follow.

Adaptation of 'The Lion and the Mouse'

A lion, with the heat oppress'd,
One day composed himself to rest;
But whilst he dozed, as he intended,
A mouse his royal back ascended;
5 Nor thought of harm as Esop* tells,
Mistaking him for something else,
And travelled over him, and round him,
And might have left him as she found him,
Had she not, tremble when you hear,
10 Tried to explore the monarch's ear!
Who straightway woke with wrath immense,
And shook his head to cast her thence.
"You rascal, what are you about,"
Said he, when he had turned her out.
15 "I'll teach you soon," the lion said,
"To make a mouse-hole in my head!"
So saying, he prepared his foot,
To crush the trembling tiny brute;
But she, the mouse, with tearful eye,
20 Implored the lion's clemency**,
Who thought it best at least to give
His little pris'ner a reprieve.

'Twas nearly twelve months after this,
The lion chanced his way to miss;
25 When pressing forward: heedless*** yet,
He got entangled in a net.
With dreadful rage he stamp'd and tore,
And straight commenced a lordly roar;
When the poor mouse who heard the noise,
30 Attended, for she knew his voice.
Then what the lion's utmost strength
Could not effect, she did at length:
With patient labour she applied
Her teeth, the net-work to divide;
35 And so at last forth issued he,
A lion, by a mouse set free.

Marmaduke Park

* Esop — *the original author of the story 'The Lion and the Mouse'*
** clemency — *mercy*
*** heedless — *reckless*

Answer these questions about the poem that you've just read.
Circle the letter that matches the correct answer.

1. Why is the lion described as "heat oppress'd" (line 1)?

    A   He is caught in a patch of sunlight.

    B   He is trapped in a net.

    C   He is very warm.

    D   He feels very cold and needs to warm up.

2. Which of these statements about the mouse's first meeting with the lion is true?

    A   The mouse thinks the lion's mouth will make a good bed for the night.

    B   The mouse challenges herself to walk on the lion.

    C   The mouse intends to wake the lion up.

    D   The mouse doesn't know she is walking on a lion.

3. The narrator portrays the lion as a:

    A   bad-tempered king.

    B   weary old man.

    C   violent brute.

    D   rowdy lord.

4. Which of the following statements is true?

    A   The narrator finds the mouse's actions humorous.

    B   The narrator expects the reader to be afraid of the lion.

    C   The narrator takes the lion's side against the mouse.

    D   The narrator's name is Esop.

TURN OVER ➡

5. According to the poem, how does the lion react to getting trapped in the net?

   A   With confusion

   B   With fury

   C   With resignation

   D   With indifference

6. What does the word "patient" (line 33) tell us about the mouse?

   A   She can work despite the lion's roars.

   B   She is happy to wait for the lion to get out of the net himself.

   C   She is quite lazy in the way she works.

   D   She is taking time to ensure the job is done well.

7. Which of the following is false?

   A   The lion's rash temperament got him trapped in the net.

   B   The lion tries to escape by breaking the net.

   C   The lion gets trapped in the net exactly a year after letting the mouse go.

   D   The mouse chews the net open.

8. Which of the following best describes the mouse's relationship to the lion over the course of the poem?

   A   His enemy, then his collaborator.

   B   His tormentor, then his saviour.

   C   His accomplice, then his servant.

   D   His prisoner, then his captor.

9. Which of the following is not mentioned in the poem?

    A   How the lion reacted to being trapped.

    B   How the lion alerted the mouse to his presence on their second meeting.

    C   Why the mouse came to save the lion.

    D   How the lion reacted to being set free.

10. Which of the following best describes the moral of the poem?

    A   A kindness is never wasted.

    B   Actions speak louder than words.

    C   Absence makes the heart grow fonder.

    D   Forgive and forget.

11. What does "Implored" (line 20) mean?

    A   Demanded

    B   Entreated

    C   Rebuffed

    D   Inquired

12. What does "reprieve" (line 22) mean?

    A   Chance

    B   Judgement

    C   Prize

    D   Pardon

END OF TEST

/ 12

Time for a break! This puzzle is a great way to practise your **logic** skills.

The Case of the Broken Vase

At 2 pm, someone knocked a vase from its table, smashing it on the floor.
Only one of the five people in the house was in the same room as the vase when it smashed, so they are the likely culprit. The location of the vase is shown by the 'X' on the diagram. The five friends were asked where they were at 2 pm, and they all gave truthful answers.
Use the answers and the diagram below to work out who knocked the vase over.

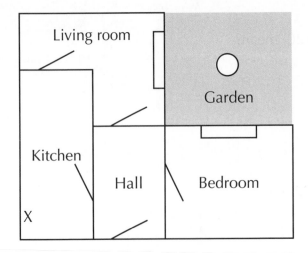

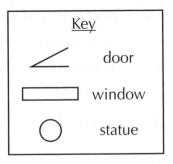

Key

/	door
▭	window
○	statue

Alan Ben left the room I was in just before 2 pm.

Ben At 2 pm, I was in the same room as Elaine.

Carol I could see the statue from the room I was in.

Dan Just before 2 pm, I saw Carol enter the room on my left. Or was it the room on my right?

Elaine The door of the room I was in was open, so I could see Dan was in the hall from 1 pm right through to 3 pm.

The person who knocked the vase over was: _____

88

You have **10 minutes** to do this test. Work as quickly and as accurately as you can.

Read this passage carefully and answer the questions that follow.

The Thai Elephant Orchestra

The Thai Elephant Conservation Centre is dedicated to the care and rehabilitation of the country's elephants. The centre focuses on supporting some of the country's captive elephants (of which there are about 2700), as well as housing sick or abandoned elephants.

5   As part of the elephants' enrichment programme, and to entertain visitors at the centre, the elephants take part in various activities. Tourists could already watch elephants paint pictures at certain shows, but Richard Lair, who runs the centre and is affectionately known in Thailand as "Professor Elephant", together with Dave Soldier, came up with another creative plan to help the residents at the centre. Traditionally,
10   elephants have responded well to music. Elephant handlers, called mahouts, have often been known to play music in order to calm their elephants. Lair and Soldier wondered whether music could be used to benefit the elephants, as well as to create an additional source of income for the centre and its mahouts. Soldier, a professor of neuroscience and a composer, was interested in exploring the musical capabilities of
15   elephants, so the two collaborated to create the Thai Elephant Orchestra.

Formed in 2000, the orchestra consists of a number of elephants from the centre, who perform for guests. They play custom-made instruments which are designed to be indestructible. Some bear resemblance to large drums, which the elephants can hit with a stick held in their trunks. Other instruments play a certain note when
20   struck, allowing elephants to create melodies. These instruments tend to use the five musical notes from the "Lanna" scale, a musical scale which is traditional in northern Thai music and is therefore familiar to the elephants.

The elephants enjoy improvising, creating pieces of music made up of deep, reverberating sounds. They can also perform rehearsed tunes, with each elephant
25   playing in time on the signal of a mahout. The orchestra has been so successful that they have even released a series of albums that showcase their musical prowess.

TURN OVER ➡

Answer these questions about the text that you've just read.
Circle the letter that matches the correct answer.

1. Which of the following best describes the primary aim of the
   Thai Elephant Conservation Centre?

   A   To entertain tourists who are visiting the area.

   B   To teach elephants to paint.

   C   To research more about elephants' relationship to music.

   D   To rehabilitate captive elephants.

2. According to the passage, which of these statements is true?

   A   There are over 2700 elephants at the Thai Elephant Conservation Centre.

   B   There are around 2700 elephants living in Thailand.

   C   Around 2700 elephants in Thailand are kept in captivity.

   D   There are around 2700 elephants in need of medical treatment in Thailand.

3. What is the most likely reason why Richard Lair is known as
   "Professor Elephant" (line 8)?

   A   He is renowned for his vast knowledge of elephants.

   B   His surname translates to "Elephant" in Thai.

   C   He works full time at a university in Thailand.

   D   He is considered by locals to have a memory as good as an elephant.

4. Who are "the residents at the conservation centre" (line 9)?

   A   People who live on site at the conservation centre.

   B   The elephants who are housed at the centre.

   C   The visitors who come to see the elephants at the conservation centre.

   D   Employees of the conservation centre.

5. According to the passage, what is a mahout?

    A   Somebody employed to teach the elephants how to paint.

    B   A conductor of the elephant orchestra.

    C   An elephant keeper.

    D   Someone studying the behaviour of elephants.

6. According to the text, which of the following are reasons why Richard Lair and Dave Soldier set up the Thai Elephant Orchestra?

    1.   To allow the mahouts to calm elephants at the conservation centre.

    2.   To secure additional funds for the upkeep of the centre.

    3.   To assist in the rehabilitation of elephants.

    4.   To research whether elephants prefer creating music or art.

    A   1 and 2

    B   2 and 3

    C   2 and 4

    D   2, 3 and 4

7. What motivated Dave Soldier to set up the Thai Elephant Orchestra?

    A   He had a passion for studying the health of elephants.

    B   He was interested in composing music for the orchestra.

    C   He wished to research how elephants responded to music.

    D   He wished to become involved in the running of the Thai Elephant Conservation Centre.

8. According to the text, why are the elephants' instruments "custom-made" (line 17)?

    A   Normal instruments would break after limited use by the elephants.

    B   Normal instruments are too small for elephants to hit accurately.

    C   The instruments needed to be louder for audiences to hear them.

    D   Dave Soldier did not want to train the elephants to use normal instruments.

TURN OVER ➡

9. According to the text, why do some of the elephants' instruments use the "Lanna scale" (line 21)?

   A   It only contains five notes so is easier for the elephants to play.

   B   It is the scale that is most popular with Thai people.

   C   It is the scale used in the music the elephants are most accustomed to.

   D   Music composed using the Lanna scale is easier to teach to elephants.

10. Which of the following best describes the music produced by the Thai Elephant Orchestra?

   A   Muffled

   B   Discordant

   C   Droning

   D   Resonant

11. What does the word "collaborated" (line 15) mean?

   A   Co-operated

   B   Sympathised

   C   Discussed

   D   Agreed

12. What does the word "prowess" (line 26) mean?

   A   Spirit

   B   Talent

   C   Appreciation

   D   Boldness

END OF TEST

/ 12

Test 22

You have **10 minutes** to do this test. Work as quickly and as accurately as you can.

Read this passage carefully and answer the questions that follow.

The New Recruits

"In height order!" shouted the sergeant, glaring at the confused line of cadets.

Immediately, Diggory Cleaves bounded up and took his position at the head of the line. He was one of the few people with any energy left after the morning's 20-kilometre run. They'd only finished lunch break 20 minutes ago, but a few sandwiches and a 30

5 minute rest seemed little help after a morning of pain.

Gemma, Dean and Ana stood back, waiting for some order to resume before joining the fray. As a line slowly appeared, Dean took his place in between Diggory and a lanky boy called Jimmy, while Gemma lined up behind Cathy. Ana was trying to work out whether she was taller or shorter than Cathy. Though she was taller, she decided to

10 slouch so she could stand with Gemma. The burden of the 5-kilogram bag that she carried on her back like the rest of the cadets made this easy.

"Right you bunch of no-goods!" cried the sergeant when the final cadet was in place. "This afternoon is the Mud Trail! Private Perry will issue you with 1 extra kilogram weight at the start line. Two extra kilograms for new recruits!"

15 Gemma's heart sank. The Mud Trail was the most infamous part of cadet training. It was 15 kilometres of running and horrendous obstacles, like the Fire Wall and the Ice Tunnel. Its path snaked around the army base, into Frinwick woods, twice taking them through the freezing river that ran through the area.

"The course record is 3 hours and 21 minutes!" boomed the sergeant. "Looking at the

20 state of you, I'll be surprised if any of you do it in under 4!"

Gemma looked at her watch. If the trail did take them 4 hours, they'd be back just before dusk and in time for supper. That wasn't taking into account the 2-kilometre run back inland from the finishing line on the beach to the base.

"Right, it's 2 o'clock!" said the sergeant. "See you at the finish line!" And before the

25 cadets even had a chance to secure their bags, the whistle was blown and they were off.

TURN OVER ➡

Answer these questions about the text that you've just read.
Circle the letter that matches the correct answer.

1. Why does Diggory Cleaves take his position "at the head of the line" (lines 2-3)?

    A   He is the tallest cadet.

    B   He is the fittest cadet.

    C   He completed the morning's activities in the fastest time.

    D   He doesn't want to have to wait at the back of the queue.

2. What time did the cadets start lunch?

    A   12:30 pm

    B   1:00 pm

    C   1:10 pm

    D   1:40 pm

3. According to the passage, Gemma, Ana and Dean were "waiting for some order to resume before joining the fray" (lines 6-7). This means:

    A   They already knew exactly where in the line they needed to stand.

    B   They wished to stay uninvolved until part of the line had been formed.

    C   They were waiting for instructions on where to stand in the queue.

    D   They were instructed to wait before joining the fight that the other cadets were having.

4. According to the passage, which of the following is true?

    A   Dean is shorter than Cathy.

    B   Gemma and Cathy are the same height.

    C   Ana is taller than Gemma.

    D   Ana is shorter than Cathy.

5. According to the text, "Gemma's heart sank" (line 15). Why did this happen?

    A   Gemma was unenthusiastic about the prospect of the Mud Trail.

    B   Gemma was worried she would be the slowest cadet.

    C   Gemma didn't like being shouted at by the sergeant.

    D   Gemma thought the sergeant was treating them unfairly.

6. When does the sergeant expect the cadets to finish the Mud Trail?

    A   An hour before supper time

    B   Around 5:30 pm

    C   Just before 6:00 pm

    D   Sometime after 6:00 pm

7. Which of the following best describes the course of the Mud Trail?

    A   Through the army base and onto the beach

    B   Through rivers by the army base and into Frinwick woods

    C   Around the army base grounds, finishing in Frinwick woods

    D   Around the army base, through Frinwick woods and onto the beach

8. According to the passage, which of the following must be false?

    A   The newest recruits must carry more weight than other recruits.

    B   Recruits must complete the Mud Trail with a bag weighing 5 kilograms.

    C   The Mud Trail involves two river crossings.

    D   The Sergeant does not intend to complete the course with the cadets.

TURN OVER ➡

9. According to the passage, where is the army base?

   A   On the coast, overlooking the sea

   B   2 km away from the beach

   C   Within Frinwick woods

   D   On the banks of a river

10. By the end of the day, how far will Gemma have run?

    A   15 km

    B   17 km

    C   35 km

    D   37 km

11. Which of the following best describes how the Sergeant treats the cadets?

    A   Harshly

    B   Solemnly

    C   Benignly

    D   Gallantly

12. Which of the following pieces of information is not included in the passage?

    A   The name of the third tallest person in the cadets.

    B   The names of two obstacles featured in the Mud Trail.

    C   The record time for the 20-kilometre run.

    D   What the cadets had for lunch on the day they did the Mud Trail.

END OF TEST

/ 12

You have **10 minutes** to do this test. Work as quickly and as accurately as you can.

Read this passage carefully and answer the questions that follow.

An extract from 'The Circular Staircase'

    Liddy and I got as far as the card-room and turned on all the lights. I tried the small entry door there, which opened on the veranda, and examined the windows. Everything was secure, and Liddy, a little less nervous now, had just pointed out to me the disgracefully dusty condition of the hard-wood floor, when suddenly the
5 lights went out. We waited a moment; I think Liddy was stunned with fright, or she would have screamed. And then I clutched her by the arm and pointed to one of the windows opening on the porch. The sudden change threw the window into relief, an oblong of greyish light, and showed us a figure standing close, peering in. As I looked it darted across the veranda and out of sight in the darkness.
10 Liddy's knees seemed to give away under her. Without a sound she sank down, leaving me staring at the window in petrified amazement. Liddy began to moan under her breath, and in my excitement I reached down and shook her.
    "Stop it," I whispered. "It's only a woman — maybe a maid of the Armstrongs'. Get up and help me find the door." She groaned again. "Very well," I said, "then I'll
15 have to leave you here. I'm going."
    She moved at that, and, holding to my sleeve, we felt our way, with numerous collisions, to the billiard-room, and from there to the drawing-room. The lights came on then, and, with the long French windows unshuttered, I had a creepy feeling that each one sheltered a peering face. In fact, in the light of what happened afterward, I
20 am pretty certain we were under surveillance during the entire ghostly evening. We hurried over the rest of the locking-up and got upstairs as quickly as we could. I left the lights all on, and our footsteps echoed cavernously. Liddy had a stiff neck the next morning, from looking back over her shoulder, and she refused to go to bed.

Mary Roberts Rinehart

TURN OVER ➡

Answer these questions about the text that you've just read.
Circle the letter that matches the correct answer.

1. According to the passage, which of the following is true?

   A   The house is in a state of disrepair.

   B   Parts of the house have not been cleaned recently.

   C   The locks on the windows of the house are broken.

   D   The lights in parts of the house do not work.

2. What initially startles Liddy?

   A   The appearance of the figure at the window.

   B   The fact that all the lights go out.

   C   The appearance of the windows in the dark.

   D   The fact that the narrator grabs her arm.

3. Which of the following details about the figure at the window must be true?

   A   It was a man.

   B   It was someone employed by the Armstrongs.

   C   It was attempting to break into the house.

   D   It did not want to be seen.

4. During the passage, the narrator stared at the window "in petrified amazement" (line 11). This means they were:

   A   so scared and shocked that they were unable to move.

   B   limp with fear.

   C   shaking because they were so frightened.

   D   surprised to see the figure, but excited by it nonetheless.

5. What caused Liddy to move in line 16 of the passage?

    A   She wanted to move away from the window.

    B   She was frightened by the prospect of being left alone.

    C   She wanted to assist the narrator in finding the door.

    D   She wished to explore the billiard-room.

6. Which of the following accurately describes the layout of the house?

    A   The card-room leads into the drawing-room.

    B   The card-room is on the top floor of the house.

    C   The card-room connects to the billiard-room.

    D   The card-room can only be accessed from the inside.

7. Why does the narrator describe the evening as "ghostly" (line 20)?

    A   They are convinced that the house is haunted.

    B   They believe the figure at the window was a ghost.

    C   They are spooked by the events that happened in the evening.

    D   The evening was dark and shadowy.

8. What is the most likely reason the narrator "left the lights all on" (lines 21-22)?

    A   They were so scared that they forgot to turn them off.

    B   So they could see when they went upstairs.

    C   To let people know they were still awake.

    D   Leaving the lights on helped to make them feel safer.

TURN OVER ➡

Test 23

9. What is the most likely reason why Liddy refused to go to bed?

    A   She was suffering from a stiff neck.

    B   She was unable to sleep with the lights on.

    C   She was too disturbed by the evening's events.

    D   She knew the sound of footsteps would keep her awake.

10. Which of the following words best describes Liddy during the passage?

    A   Distraught

    B   Fatigued

    C   Melancholy

    D   Mournful

11. In the context of the passage, what does "groaned" (line 14) mean?

    A   Screamed

    B   Whimpered

    C   Whispered

    D   Gasped

12. What does "surveillance" (line 20) mean?

    A   Control

    B   Guard

    C   Scrutiny

    D   Vigilance

END OF TEST

/ 12

Time for a break! This puzzle is a great way to practise your **logic** and **word-making** skills.

Riddle Round-Up

Cowboy Jessie's cows have gone exploring and he doesn't know where they've gone. Solve the riddles below to find out where each cow is hiding.

Daisy: My first is in curb and also in cab,
My second's in flank and also in stab,
My third is in rinse but not in trick,
My fourth is in skill but more so in kick.

Daisy is in the _____

Marigold: My first is in charm and also in bewitch,
My second's in sport and also in polo,
My third is in table and also in stool,
My fourth is in anger and also in jealousy,
My fifth is in lend but isn't in dice,

Marigold is in the _____

Snowdrop: My first is in star and also in stripe,
My second's in write and also in type,
My third is in stage but not in show,
My fourth in is bubble and less so in blow,
My fifth is in werewolf, troll and elf,
My last is in step and also in shelf.

Snowdrop is in the _____

You have **10 minutes** to do this test. Work as quickly and as accurately as you can.

Read this passage carefully and answer the questions that follow.

Patrick's Attic Blunder

Patrick turned the key and pushed. The attic door swung open with a resounding clatter. Hoping the commotion hadn't woken the rest of his family, Patrick tiptoed across the threshold and into the darkness of the forbidden room. The excitement of finally seeing what his grandparents had kept up here for so long was overwhelming
5   and, as he swung his torch around this magpie's nest with wild abandon, his expectations were soon met.

The attic was the intriguing treasure trove that Patrick had always dreamt it would be: an old rocking chair; a pile of what might be paperback novels or worn diaries; moth-eaten clothes that appeared to belong to another century...
10 Patrick crept around the room, taking in the shelves of wonders and minding not to trip on the old toys and ornaments strewn across the floor. Suddenly, amongst the array of antiquated objects, something caught Patrick's attention. On a table at the far end of the attic sat a chessboard, and peering up at him from it were thirty-two dust-encrusted chess pieces. And they were no ordinary chess pieces — as he
15 checked them over, Patrick could see that whoever had carved them had taken considerable care. The kings and queens, resplendent in intricately patterned robes, stood mightily at either end of the board, flanked by the other important pieces. In front of them, the plucky pawns all stood in different poses.

Patrick wanted to examine these exquisite figures more closely. He picked the
20 chessboard up, careful not to let the pieces tumble into the shadows at his feet. With no free hands, he wedged the torch precariously between his elbow and side.

He heard a voice from outside the room. "Hello?" it called questioningly.

Patrick panicked — he had absent-mindedly left the attic door open, the key still in the lock! Now, his blunder would allow his family to find him easily. There was
25 only one course of action: he would have to retreat to a corner of the attic and hide. Patrick delicately placed the chess set back on the table and made his move.

Answer these questions about the text that you've just read.
Circle the letter that matches the correct answer.

1. The attic is described as a "magpie's nest" (line 5).
   This means:

   A   Patrick has seen birds flying into and out of the attic.

   B   the attic is full of interesting items his grandparents had collected.

   C   the attic is high off the ground.

   D   the attic is full of shiny objects.

2. Which of the following best describes Patrick's reaction to entering the attic?

   A   Masked disappointment

   B   Tempered glee

   C   Undisguised irritation

   D   Uncontrollable exuberance

3. Why doesn't Patrick want to wake his family when he enters the attic?

   A   He wants to surprise them with the chess set later.

   B   He doesn't want to disturb them since he thinks they are tired.

   C   He doesn't want to alert them to the fact he's in the attic.

   D   He doesn't want to share the objects he finds with them.

4. Which of the following does Patrick not find in the attic?

   A   Books

   B   Toys

   C   Furniture

   D   Photographs

TURN OVER ➡

5. The moth-eaten clothes are described as belonging to "another century" (line 9). This means:

    A   the clothes do not belong to Patrick's grandparents.

    B   the clothes must be a really old family heirloom.

    C   the clothes look old and out of place.

    D   the clothes look like they are from the future.

6. Which of the following best describes the attic?

    A   Secluded and pristine

    B   Dim and untidy

    C   Dusty and opulent

    D   Private and bare

7. According to the text, why does Patrick pick up the chess set?

    A   He wants to inspect the chess pieces more thoroughly.

    B   He wants to play a game of chess with his family.

    C   He wishes to sell the chessboard because he thinks it is valuable.

    D   He knows it is the only thing in reach he can look at more closely.

8. Which of the following statements is true?

    A   Patrick is not concerned about losing one or two chess pieces.

    B   Patrick thinks the pawns all look identical to one another.

    C   The king and queen are positioned around the other important pieces.

    D   Patrick carries the chessboard with both hands.

9. Why does the person outside the room call "questioningly" (line 22)?

    A   They can see a figure in the attic but don't know who it is.

    B   They can see the open door and want to know if anyone's inside.

    C   They can see Patrick with an object and want to know what it is.

    D   They can hear Patrick moving and want to know what he's doing.

10. At the end of the passage, why did Patrick panic (line 23)?

    A   He realised he would have to leave the chess set in order to hide.

    B   He realised his carelessness was likely going to get him caught.

    C   He could see there weren't many good hiding places.

    D   He knew he wasn't going to be able to make a quick exit.

11. What does "commotion" (line 2) mean?

    A   Bother

    B   Outbreak

    C   Racket

    D   Argument

12. What does "resplendent" (line 16) mean?

    A   Magnificent

    B   Garish

    C   Exorbitant

    D   Affluent

END OF TEST

/ 12

You have **10 minutes** to do this test. Work as quickly and as accurately as you can.

Read this passage carefully and answer the questions that follow.

Wangari Maathai

On Sunday 5th June 1977, the World Environment Day of that year, a small group of campaigners planted seven trees in a park in Nairobi, the capital of Kenya. The seven trees were the start of a campaign that within a few decades would see fifty-one million trees planted throughout Africa. By doing this, the campaigners were
5 tackling a long-standing problem.

Planting these trees was the idea of Wangari Maathai. Born in rural Kenya in 1940, Maathai went on to study in the United States and Germany before returning to her home country, where she became an activist and environmentalist. In 1974, Maathai focused her attention specifically on issues surrounding deforestation. She noticed that,
10 by chopping down trees for firewood, her fellow citizens were causing the soil to dry out, which in turn meant less food could be grown. For Maathai, planting trees was the simplest solution: trees could accumulate rainwater, maintain nutrients in the soil and even supply people with fruit to eat. So, in 1977, she founded the Green Belt Movement.

After the planting in Nairobi, Maathai's Green Belt Movement continued its
15 campaign by handing out free saplings to Kenyan women, encouraging them to grow their own trees. The women involved were paid a small amount for every tree they planted and cared for, creating an incentive to plant more than they would need for firewood alone. Women could also take any excess wood they harvested to market. Before long, women were growing tree nurseries together. These nurseries helped the
20 environment, provided income for families and allowed Kenyan women to congregate at a time when public meetings were banned. These women later became involved with Maathai's movement in efforts to combat poverty, forest destruction and disease.

For her environmental work and providing African women with a voice, one of the Nobel committees decided that Maathai was a worthy winner of their Peace Prize. In
25 2004, she became the first African woman to win the prestigious award, joining fellow African Peace laureates like Nelson Mandela.

Answer these questions about the text that you've just read.
Circle the letter that matches the correct answer.

1. Why did the group choose the 5th of June to plant their trees in Nairobi?

   A   It was a Sunday, which meant the parks would be quieter.

   B   It was World Environment Day, which Wangari Maathai founded.

   C   It was World Environment Day, so planting trees was a suitable activity.

   D   It was a Sunday, so many people could attend the planting as they weren't at work.

2. Where was Wangari Maathai born?

   A   In Nairobi, the capital of Kenya.

   B   In the Kenyan countryside.

   C   In an urban area of Kenya.

   D   In the United States.

3. According to the text, what did Maathai believe was causing crops to fail in Kenya?

   A   Cutting down trees which affected the soil.

   B   Fires getting out of control and burning the crops.

   C   A lack of rainfall over several months.

   D   Trees that, when planted, absorbed the water from the soil.

4. Which of the following best describes the Green Belt Movement?

   A   An organisation focusing on eradicating inequality.

   B   A charity that aids Kenyan women in increasing their incomes.

   C   A political body campaigning for women's rights.

   D   A campaign focusing on increasing the number of trees in Kenya.

TURN OVER ➡

5. Why were Kenyan women initially likely to take the saplings from Maathai's group?

    A   They were excited to be able to work with friends to grow tree nurseries.

    B   The Green Belt Movement forced them to plant the saplings.

    C   There was no risk in taking the saplings because they didn't cost anything.

    D   They expected the trees to produce large amounts of firewood quickly.

6. What financial incentive did Maathai give tree planters?

    A   Money for excess firewood.

    B   Money for each sapling grown.

    C   Money for positive changes to the soil in the local area.

    D   Money for crops grown.

7. The Green Belt Movement made "efforts to combat poverty" (line 22). This means:

    A   it made attempts to reduce poverty.

    B   its actions led to an increase in poverty.

    C   it started fights in order to prevent poverty.

    D   it joined forces to ignore poverty.

8. Which of the following statements is true?

    A   Maathai was the first African person to win a Nobel Prize.

    B   Maathai won the Nobel Peace Prize for halting deforestation.

    C   Nobel Prize winners are decided by a public vote.

    D   It was over 25 years between Maathai's founding of the Green Belt Movement and her being awarded the Nobel Peace Prize.

9. Which of the following were consequences of the movement to plant trees throughout Kenya?

    1.   The soil improved in ways that let people grow more food.
    2.   The price of firewood increased as more of it became available.
    3.   Kenyan women united to solve problems.
    4.   An additional seven trees were planted in capital cities throughout Africa.

    A   1 and 3
    B   2 and 3
    C   1, 3 and 4
    D   2, 3 and 4

10. Which of the following best describes Wangari Maathai?
    A   Intelligent and egocentric
    B   Unimaginative and considerate
    C   Resourceful and compassionate
    D   Uneducated and neighbourly

11. What does "accumulate" (line 12) mean?
    A   Furnish
    B   Increase
    C   Amass
    D   Supply

12. What does "prestigious" (line 25) mean?
    A   Expensive
    B   Acclaimed
    C   Contented
    D   Fortunate

END OF TEST

/ 12

You have **10 minutes** to do this test. Work as quickly and as accurately as you can.

Read this passage carefully and answer the questions that follow.

The Ten o'Clock Monster

I was out of breath, my shoulders were straining with the weight of my backpack and my feet were beginning to throb in my ill-fitting shoes. But I was determined to be the first to get there, so the pain did little to prolong my ascent up the mountain. Finally, I reached the top. In front of me was, in my opinion, the greatest view on
5   earth: Rio de Janeiro, my home, the morning sun glistening off the windows of the skyscrapers.

In that moment, I felt the vitality of the city more than I ever have before. Looking down on everyone, I thought about how small and insignificant they all were compared to the inconceivable vastness of Earth and its unknown wonders.

10   From the summit of Corcovado Mountain, I could see practically the entire city. This included the instantly recognisable Sugarloaf Mountain, jutting out from the edge of the city into the ocean, and the white sands of Copacabana Beach. But my attention was drawn out to the sea, where I could already see some ripples. Though I had only ever seen the upcoming spectacle from down in the city, my friend Maria
15 (who watched it from the Corcovado last month) had told me that such movements in the water were the unmistakable prelude to what was about to happen.

In the fifteen minutes since my arrival on the summit, a crowd had joined me on the Corcovado. Most were tourists, clinging to binoculars. I stood, quivering in nervous anticipation, as I counted down the seconds, waiting for ten o'clock to arrive.

20   Sure enough, at ten o'clock precisely, a volcano of water spurted from the ocean just beyond the Sugarloaf. Scaly like a lizard's, the monster's head rose out of the water atop its protruding neck. Suddenly, the creature stood upright, and we could see its body and its long, ape-like arms. It strode unwaveringly from the sea, creating surges of water as it skirted the Sugarloaf towards the beach. Despite having seen it
25 many times now, the way this juggernaut shifted the whole ocean before it still amazed me. At a height of 500 metres, it cast a shadow over the entire city, and for a terrifying moment I wondered whether it would actually return to the sea as it had before.

Answer these questions about the text that you've just read.
Circle the letter that matches the correct answer.

1. Why does the narrator walk so quickly up the mountain?

   A   To reach the top in a faster time than the record set by Maria last month.

   B   To beat the tourists and other people to the top of the mountain.

   C   To gain the best view of Rio de Janeiro.

   D   To shorten the time they have to deal with the pain from their shoes.

2. Why might the narrator's belief that Corcovado Mountain has
   "the greatest view on earth" (lines 4-5) be slightly skewed?

   A   The narrator has only climbed one mountain in their life.

   B   It is a particularly bright and sunny day.

   C   The narrator's opinion is affected by those of the tourists.

   D   The view from the mountain is over the narrator's home town.

3. The narrator says they feel "the vitality of the city" (line 7).
   This means:

   A   the narrator senses how lively the city is.

   B   the narrator realises that people in the city are starting to wake up.

   C   the narrator comprehends the number of people in the city.

   D   the narrator believes that the city's buildings are alive.

4. The ripples are described as "the unmistakable prelude to what was about to
   happen" (line 16). What does this tell you about the ripples?

   A   They reveal the weather is about to take a turn for the worse.

   B   They show the creature is approaching the surface of the water.

   C   They suggest the creature is going to walk towards the city.

   D   They indicate tourists are congregating in boats to watch the creature.

TURN OVER ➡

5. Which of the following best describes how the narrator feels just before 10:00?

   A   Anxious

   B   Distressed

   C   Horrified

   D   Dismayed

6. As the creature rises from the ocean, the narrator states "a volcano of water spurted from the ocean" (line 20). This means:

   A   the creature has made the water extremely hot.

   B   steam rises from the water as the creature ascends.

   C   the water looks like it is erupting from the ocean.

   D   the water is near Sugarloaf Mountain, which used to be a volcano.

7. Which of the following statements is false?

   A   The creature can walk on two legs.

   B   The creature has long arms relative to the rest of its body.

   C   The creature emerges from the ocean head-first.

   D   The creature is very smooth to the touch.

8. According to the text, the creature strode "unwaveringly" (line 23).
   This means:

   A   the creature creates waves as he moves through the water.

   B   the creature doesn't stop moving.

   C   the creature walks slowly.

   D   the creature doesn't feel tired as a result of rising from the sea.

9. Which of the following is the narrator most amazed by?

   A   The creature's colossal size.

   B   The way the creature moves.

   C   The power and strength of the creature.

   D   The creature's strange appearance.

10. At the end of the text, what is it that the narrator is most likely afraid of?

   A   That the creature might return to the sea.

   B   That the creature might not return to the sea.

   C   That someone might spot the creature before they do.

   D   That the movement of the creature might create a tsunami.

11. What does "prolong" (line 3) mean?

   A   Lengthen

   B   Spoil

   C   Halt

   D   Taint

12. In the context of the passage, what does "inconceivable" (line 9) mean?

   A   Illogical

   B   Erroneous

   C   Incredible

   D   Irrational

END OF TEST

/ 12

Time for a break! This puzzle is a great way to practise your **logic** skills.

Bookshelf Sequence

Samantha has a very particular way of organising her bookshelf.
She arranges her books from left to right using the following rules:

- The encyclopedia must go next to a novel.

- The novels must be grouped together and so should the history books.

- The novels should be ordered alphabetically according to the author's surname.

- The history books should be in order of the date in
  their title, starting with the earliest date.

- The dictionary must have a history book on its left and a novel on its right.

- Neither of the two tallest books can go in the very middle of the bookshelf.

The nine books on Samantha's bookshelf, shown below, are currently in the wrong
order. Write the numbers 1 to 9 in the boxes below each book to show which order
the books should go in, using the rules above. Number 1 should mark the book
that goes on the far left. Number 9 should mark the book that goes on the far right.

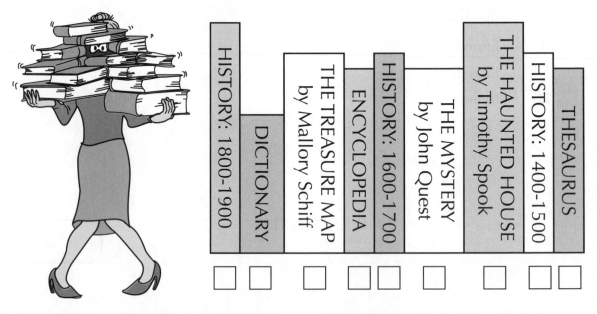

You have **10 minutes** to do this test. Work as quickly and as accurately as you can.

Read this passage carefully and answer the questions that follow.

An extract from 'Eric'

"Eric, you are a thief!" He thought he heard his brother Vernon's voice utter the
words thrillingly distinct; but it was conscience who had borrowed the voice, and, sick
with horror, he began to shake the money out of his pockets again into the box. He was
only just in time; he had barely locked the box, and put it in its place, when he heard
5   the sound of voices and footsteps on the stairs. He had no time to take out the key and
put it back where he found it, and had hardly time to slip into his own study again,
when the boys had reached the landing.

They were Duncan and Montagu, and as they passed the door, Eric pretended to be
plunged in books.

10   "Hallo, Eric! grinding* as usual," said Duncan, good-humouredly; but he only got a
sickly smile in reply.

"What! are you the only fellow in the studies?" asked Montagu. "I was nearly sure I
heard some one moving about as we came up stairs."

"I don't think there's any one here but me," said Eric, "and I'm going a walk now."

15   He closed his books with a bang, flew down stairs, and away through the play-ground
towards the shore. But he could not so escape his thoughts. "Eric, you are a thief! Eric,
you are a thief!" rang in his ear. "Yes," he thought; "I am even a thief. Oh, good God,
yes, even a thief, for I had actually stolen the money, until I changed my mind. What
if they should discover the key in the box, knowing that I was the only fellow up stairs?

20 Oh, mercy, mercy, mercy!"

It was a lonely place, and he flung himself down and hid his face in the coarse grass,
trying to cool the wild burning of his brow. And as he lay he thrust his hand into the
guilty pocket! Good heavens! there was something still there. He pulled it out; it was
a sovereign. Then he was a thief, even actually. Oh, everything was against him; and

25 starting to his feet, he flung the accursed gold over the rocks far into the sea.

*grinding — *working hard*   **Frederic Farrar**

TURN OVER ➡

Answer these questions about the text that you've just read.
Circle the letter that matches the correct answer.

1. What caused Eric to return the money to the box?

   A   He was afraid of being discovered by Duncan and Montagu.

   B   His brother told him to return the coins.

   C   He began to feel unwell.

   D   He began to feel guilty.

2. According to the text, Eric "pretended to be plunged in books" (lines 8-9). This means:

   A   he gave the impression of working hard.

   B   he was carrying a large pile of books.

   C   he was carefully reading a range of books.

   D   he was hiding behind a stack of books.

3. Eric gave Duncan a "sickly smile" (line 11). This means:

   A   the smile makes Duncan feel nauseous.

   B   the smile isn't entirely genuine.

   C   the smile is incredibly broad.

   D   the smile is more of a grimace than a smile.

4. Montagu says "I was nearly sure I heard some one moving about as we came up stairs" (lines 12-13). Who had Montagu heard?

   A   Duncan

   B   Montagu's own footsteps

   C   Eric

   D   No-one — he had misheard the sound of footsteps.

5. According to the passage, which of the following statements is true?

   A   Duncan is unpleasant towards Eric.

   B   Duncan thinks Eric spends a lot of time studying.

   C   Duncan knows Eric is prone to thieving.

   D   Duncan often worries about how much time Eric spends in the studies.

6. Which of the following words best describes "the studies" in line 12?

   A   Disused

   B   Rejected

   C   Deserted

   D   Neglected

7. What makes Eric concerned that the other boys will know he tried to steal the money in the box?

   A   He knows he has forgotten to return one of the coins.

   B   He hasn't left the box exactly as he found it.

   C   He has left the box open.

   D   He hasn't locked the box.

8. What caused the "wild burning" of Eric's brow in line 22?

   A   He was distressed about his recent actions.

   B   It was sunny and his brow was sunburnt.

   C   He was flushed after his walk.

   D   He was suffering from a fever.

TURN OVER ➡

           Test 27

9. Why does the author describe Eric's pocket as "guilty" (line 23)?

   A   The pocket was where he had put the money when he first took it.

   B   The pocket contained many stolen items.

   C   The trousers once belonged to a criminal.

   D   Eric knows that the pocket still contains a stolen item.

10. What is the most likely reason why Eric throws the coin "over the rocks far into the sea" (line 25)?

   A   He intends to get rid of the coin so he isn't tempted to spend it.

   B   He wants to see how far he can throw the coin.

   C   He knows somebody has already seen him with the coin.

   D   He wishes to get rid of the evidence of his theft.

11. What does "good-humouredly" (line 10) mean?

   A   Comically

   B   Cheerfully

   C   Mockingly

   D   Affectionately

12. What does "accursed" (line 25) mean?

   A   Haunted

   B   Unlucky

   C   Infuriating

   D   Detestable

END OF TEST

/ 12

You have **10 minutes** to do this test. Work as quickly and as accurately as you can.

Read this passage carefully and answer the questions that follow.

The South West Coast Path

Weaving around the rugged coasts from north Somerset to south Dorset, the South West Coast Path is England's longest waymarked footpath, passing through four counties: Somerset, Cornwall, Devon and Dorset. It's over 1000 km long and runs over a landscape that rises and falls, so those who wish to complete the entire stretch can expect a fair climb
5   — the total ascent over the path equates to climbing Everest four times.
Historically, the paths were created as a way for coastguards to patrol the cliffs so they could watch out for smugglers on the lower beaches. However, since 1978, when the final stretch of paths was opened, it has become a huge draw for visitors and generates millions for the local economy.
10   Starting in Minehead, on the boundaries of the Exmoor National Park, the official route traces the coast anti-clockwise to Poole. Almost half of the 630-mile trail is in Cornwall, where the route explores the most southerly and westerly points of the UK mainland, Lizard Point and Land's End respectively. The trail goes from Marsland Mouth in the north of Cornwall to Rame Head and the Tamar Estuary near the Cornish border in the south east.
15   The route then moves into Devon before crossing the Dorset border just before Lyme Regis.
The coastal paths take in stunning panoramas and villages that are rich in cultural history. About 70% of the coastal path is in either National Parks or areas which have protected status. They include Tintagel, King Arthur's legendary castle on the Cornish cliffs. The stretch along Exmoor Coastal Heaths (in the National Park) is recognised as a Site of
20   Special Scientific Interest due to the diversity of species there.
The route attracts walkers of all abilities, taking an average of around 8 weeks to complete. Ultra runners have set much faster times, with the record (set in 2016) standing at just under 11 days. Though many take on the challenge for pleasure, a number of walkers are sponsored for their endeavours and many charities benefit from this, including the South
25   West Coast Path Association (SWCPA). With upkeep costs of about £1000 per mile of path per year, the work of the SWCPA is vital for ensuring this great trail stands for years to come.

TURN OVER ➡

Answer these questions about the text that you've just read.
Circle the letter that matches the correct answer.

1. Which of the following best describes the main historical use of the South West Coast Path?

    A   To attract holiday-makers to the South West.

    B   To provide ultra runners with new, difficult challenges.

    C   To allow coastguards to transport smugglers to local prisons.

    D   To give the authorities a vantage point over beaches.

2. According to the text, where is Minehead?

    A   North Somerset

    B   South Devon

    C   South Somerset

    D   North Devon

3. According to the passage, which of the following statements must be true?

    A   30% of the South West Coast Path is through towns.

    B   Around 500 km of the South West Coast Path are in Cornwall.

    C   The most interesting parts of the South West Coast Path are in Cornwall.

    D   The South West Coast Path is the most popular tourist attraction
            in the South West.

4. Which of the following places is on the border between Devon
    and Cornwall?

    A   Lizard Point

    B   Land's End

    C   Tamar Estuary

    D   Lyme Regis

5. Which of the following pieces of information is not mentioned in the text?

   A   Where the suggested route starts and ends.

   B   The longest ascent on the South West Coast Path.

   C   The name of the most southerly point in Great Britain.

   D   The county in which Lyme Regis is located.

6. Which of the following words would not be used to describe the South West Coast Path?

   A   Popular

   B   Picturesque

   C   Exclusive

   D   Undulating

7. Which of the following areas is not in Cornwall?

   A   Lizard Point

   B   Tintagel

   C   Rame Head

   D   Exmoor Coastal Heath

8. Which of the following is not a reason why people might visit the South West Coast Path?

   A   To spot a wide variety of animal and bird species.

   B   To visit the burial place of King Arthur.

   C   To learn about traditional Cornish culture.

   D   To enjoy some of Britain's most scenic views.

TURN OVER ➡

9. Which of the following statements is true?

    A   Most people who walk the South West Coast Path do it for charity.

    B   Most people chose to run, rather than walk, the South West Coast Path.

    C   Most runners can expect to complete the South West Coast Path in 10 days.

    D   Most people take just over 55 days to walk the whole of the
            South West Coast Path.

10. Which of the following would you not expect to find on the
    South West Coast Path today?

    A   Runners

    B   Hikers

    C   Smugglers

    D   Scientists

11. Which of the following statements must be false?

    A   Both charities and local businesses benefit from people walking the
            South West Costal Path.

    B   The annual upkeep of the South West Coast Path costs over £1 million.

    C   Every kilometre of the South West Coast Path costs under £1000 to maintain.

    D   The costs for maintaining the South West Coast Path include money for
            rebuilding paths.

12. Which of the following best describes the South West Coast Path Association?

    A   A charity that works to protect the South West Coast Path.

    B   A group of people who frequently walk the South West Coast Path.

    C   An organisation that sponsors a variety of different charities.

    D   A company that works to extend the length of the South West Coast Path.

END OF TEST

/ 12

You have **10 minutes** to do this test. Work as quickly and as accurately as you can.

Read this passage carefully and answer the questions that follow.

Library of Alexandria

For many people, the Library of Alexandria occupies a place in history somewhere between fiction and fact. Its reported scale and grandeur give it an almost legendary status, but significant evidence survives to support the idea that the historical library was indeed as large and sophisticated as legend tells.

5   Located in Egypt, the Library of Alexandria was likely built under the instruction of a Macedonian general, Ptolemy I Soter, a successor of Alexander the Great, the famous king after whom the region is named. It was dedicated to the Muses, the goddesses in Greek mythology who inspired science, literature and art. Between the Library's construction (in around 300 B.C.) and the time when Egypt fell under control of the

10 Romans in around 30 B.C., Alexandria had been a hub of scholarship.

Since the library no longer exists, it's difficult to know exactly what its layout was like or quite how extensive its archives were. The library itself is thought to have consisted of a series of meeting and reading rooms, areas to eat and relax, lecture halls, and, of course, chambers containing shelves to house the monumental number

15 of documents owned by the Library. Some estimates put the quantity of scrolls in the Library at around 400,000. Many documents were acquired by copying the original document onto fresh parchment. Any single text — depending on its length — could be spread over multiple scrolls and every text was stored methodically in the library.

Unfortunately, none of the original library survives today and the cause of its

20 destruction remains a mystery. One contested theory is that during Julius Caesar's siege of the city around 20 years before Egypt fell to Rome, an uncontrollable fire destroyed the Library and many of its scrolls. Other people believe it is more likely that the library declined gradually, suffering several acts of destruction over many years.

Now, a different library has been constructed to replace this lost treasure. The

25 Bibliotheca Alexandrina was built to both commemorate the great library, as well as revive the area, so it could once more become a centre of learning.

TURN OVER ➡

Answer these questions about the text that you've just read.
Circle the letter that matches the correct answer.

1. According to the text, the Library of Alexandria "occupies a place in history somewhere between fiction and fact" (lines 1-2). This means:

    A   the Library contained a mixture of fact and fiction texts.

    B   most of what we know about the Library comes from stories.

    C   not all accounts about the Library of Alexandria are true.

    D   many people doubt that the Library existed at all.

2. According to the passage, who was Ptolemy I Soter?

    A   A high-ranking army officer

    B   The son of a king

    C   An academic

    D   A figure from Greek mythology

3. Why does the text describe Alexandria as a "hub of scholarship" (line 10)?

    A   It was a place where there were lots of schools.

    B   It was a centre for learning and research.

    C   It was the influence for modern universities.

    D   Most of the people who lived there were scientists.

4. Which of the following statements best describes the purpose of the Library of Alexandria?

    A   To create a space where information could be collected, created and shared.

    B   To provide somewhere to worship the Greek Muses.

    C   To provide rooms where Egyptians could sleep and dine.

    D   To provide a space for scribes to make copies of thousands of scrolls.

5. Which of the following words would not have been used to describe the Library of Alexandria when it stood?

   A   Prominent

   B   Revered

   C   Capacious

   D   Unsystematic

6. According to the text, when did Julius Caesar besiege Alexandria?

   A   Approximately 60 BC

   B   Approximately 50 BC

   C   Approximately 20 BC

   D   Approximately 10 BC

7. According to the text, which of the following statements best describes one theory about Caesar's involvement with the Library?

   A   Julius Caesar intentionally destroyed the Library of Alexandria.

   B   Julius Caesar campaigned to move the Library of Alexandria to Rome.

   C   Julius Caesar invaded Alexandria to capture the library there.

   D   Julius Caesar's invasion of Alexandria resulted in the Library of Alexandria burning down.

8. Which of the following words best describes the history of the Library?

   A   Rejected

   B   Disputed

   C   Trite

   D   Disjointed

TURN OVER ➡

9. Which of the following best describes why the Library of Alexandria is considered a "lost treasure" (line 24)?

    A   The Library would be a unique and important historical structure if it still stood.

    B   If the Library stood today, it would be worth lots of money.

    C   Much gold was lost when the Library was destroyed.

    D   The loss of the Library prevents us from finding out about the Roman Empire.

10. Which of the following describe why the Bibliotheca Alexandrina was built?

    1.   To celebrate the greatness of the original Library of Alexandria.

    2.   To provide a site to house modern Alexandria's collection of ancient scrolls.

    3.   To increase the amount of research and study practised in the area.

    4.   To honour the academics who used to work at the original library.

    A   1 and 2

    B   1 and 3

    C   1, 2 and 4

    D   2, 3 and 4

11. What does the word "monumental" (line 14) mean?

    A   Memorial

    B   Immense

    C   Celebratory

    D   Revolutionary

12. What does the word "revive" (line 26) mean?

    A   Reinvigorate

    B   Overhaul

    C   Rescue

    D   Animate

END OF TEST

/ 12

Puzzles 10

Time for a break! This puzzle is a great way to practise your **word-making** skills.

Honeycomb Words

The honeycombs below each contain some hidden seven-letter words. Each word is hidden in a hexagon, running clockwise or anti-clockwise, as in the example shown on the right. The final letter of the word is found in the centre of the hexagon. Each honeycomb letter can be used in more than one of the hexagons.

Find each of the hidden words using the clues below. The last letter of each word spells out a secret, bee-related word.

Word: **CAPITAL**
Central letter: **L**

1. Takes a risk: _ _ _ _ _ _ _

2. A multicoloured arc: _ _ _ _ _ _ _

3. A mathematical rule: _ _ _ _ _ _ _

4. More magnificent: _ _ _ _ _ _ _

5. An accurate drawing: _ _ _ _ _ _ _

SECRET WORD: _ _ _ _ _ _

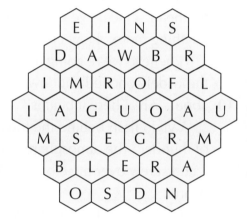

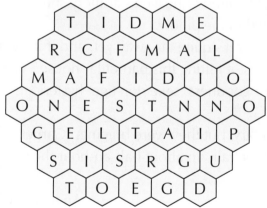

1. Someone's belief: _ _ _ _ _ _ _

2. Complete quiet: _ _ _ _ _ _ _

3. The vehicles on a road: _ _ _ _ _ _ _ _

4. Far away: _ _ _ _ _ _ _

5. A difficult situation: _ _ _ _ _ _ _

6. Walk unsteadily: _ _ _ _ _ _ _

SECRET WORD: _ _ _ _ _ _ _

You have **10 minutes** to do this test. Work as quickly and as accurately as you can.

Read this passage carefully and answer the questions that follow.

An extract from 'The Luckiest Girl in the School'

"We've done our best, and it depends now whether we've luck in the questions," said Winona. "I think we'd better put the books away. We shall only muddle ourselves if we try any more to-night. Aunt Harriet says we're not to get up at five to-morrow. We shall have quite a hard enough day as it is."

5   "It wouldn't be much use," said Garnet, thrusting back the hair from her hot forehead. "I feel I've taken in the utmost my brains can hold. There's no room for anything more. How close the air is!"

"I believe we're going to have another storm," replied Winona, leaning out of the widely opened window, to gaze at the lurid sky. "There's a feeling of electricity

10 about. Ah! There it begins!"

A vivid flash behind the tower of the old Minster* was followed by a long rumble of thunder. The atmosphere was painfully oppressive. Again a white streak ran like a corkscrew over the clouds, and a louder peal resounded. The storm was drawing nearer.

15 "Come from the window, Winona. It's not safe!"

Garnet was terribly afraid of thunder. The electricity in the air has a powerful effect upon some temperaments, and at the first sound of heaven's artillery she was crouching beside her bed, with her head buried in the pillow.

"Don't be a silly ostrich!" retorted her chum. "It's quite far away yet, and if it does

20 come, the chances are a thousand to one against it hitting this particular house. Why, you weren't half so scared of Zeppelins**! For goodness' sake don't get hysterical! Show some pluck!"

Winona's remarks might not be complimentary, but they were bracing. Garnet laughed nervously, and consented to sit upon a chair. In about half-an-hour the

25 storm blew over, leaving a clear sky and stars.

Angela Brazil

* Minster — *a large church*

** Zeppelins — *large airships used in the First World War*

Answer these questions about the text that you've just read. Circle the letter that matches the correct answer.

1. Which of the following statements must be false?

   A   Winona thinks that how well they do in the exam will depend on the questions asked.

   B   Winona thinks that if they revise more they may confuse themselves.

   C   Winona thinks that they have not done their utmost to prepare for the exam.

   D   Winona expects that the exam won't be straightforward.

2. Why does Aunt Harriet suggest that Winona and Garnet are "not to get up at five to-morrow" (lines 3-4)?

   A   Aunt Harriet does not want to be disturbed too early.

   B   Aunt Harriet wants Winona and Garnet to have sufficient sleep.

   C   Aunt Harriet does not want Winona and Garnet to oversleep.

   D   Aunt Harriet thinks Winona and Garnet should wake up earlier to allow more time to prepare for the exam.

3. Why does Garnet not want to revise any more that evening?

   A   She has learnt as much as she can manage.

   B   She thinks she knows all there is to know.

   C   She has become distracted by the oncoming storm.

   D   She is suffering from a headache.

4. Garnet states: "How close the air is!" (line 7). This means:

   A   that it is incredibly dark.

   B   there is a hot breeze.

   C   that it is humid and stuffy.

   D   there is a thick mist.

TURN OVER ➡

5. Which of the following words best describes Winona's response to the storm?

   A   Apprehensive

   B   Captivated

   C   Astonished

   D   Jubilant

6. According to the text, how do we know that the "storm was drawing nearer" (lines 13-14)?

   A   The atmosphere was becoming more oppressive.

   B   The sound of thunder was growing stronger.

   C   The flashes of lightning were becoming more regular.

   D   The storm clouds were moving towards the Minster.

7. The text says that the "electricity in the air has a powerful effect on some temperaments" (lines 16-17). This means that:

   A   Storms upset some people more than others.

   B   Some storms are more destructive than others.

   C   Some people enjoy storms.

   D   Some people can sense thunderstorms before they happen.

8. What does the narrator describe as "heaven's artillery" (line 17)?

   A   The flashes of lightning in the sky.

   B   The roar of the wind.

   C   The sound of heavy rain.

   D   The crashes of thunder.

9. Why does Winona think that Garnet should not be afraid of the storm?

   A   The storm will not come anywhere near them.

   B   They are inside so are sheltered from the thunder.

   C   The storm will stop attacks from Zeppelins.

   D   The likelihood of their building being struck by lightning is incredibly low.

10. Which of the following best describes "Winona's remarks" (line 23)?

   A   Flattering and inspiring

   B   Insulting and insightful

   C   Critical and invigorating

   D   Sensitive and encouraging

11. What does "lurid" (line 9) mean?

   A   Ablaze

   B   Glaring

   C   Cloudless

   D   Multicoloured

12. What does "pluck" (line 22) mean?

   A   Maturity

   B   Courage

   C   Fear

   D   Responsibility

END OF TEST

/ 12

You have **10 minutes** to do this test. Work as quickly and as accurately as you can.

Read this passage carefully and answer the questions that follow.

Space Debris

Space debris has been accumulating around our planet since the 1950s. Though some natural debris exists in Earth's orbit (such as rocks flying through space), the dawn of the Space Age has seen huge amounts of man-made debris put into space.

In 2013, it was estimated that over 170 million pieces of space debris were in orbit
5   around Earth. Space debris can range from entire decommissioned satellites and sections of old rockets, to tiny pieces of shrapnel created by collisions between objects. As of 2013, around 670,000 pieces of debris are 1-10 cm across, and a significant number (around 29,000) are larger.

Space debris poses a problem, as it can collide with functional objects. For
10   example, in 2009, a deactivated Russian satellite hit an operational US satellite, Iridium 33. Though the loss of the US communications satellite was the initial problem, a greater and enduring threat was posed by the thousands of debris shards created by the impact. These shards could have gone on to collide with other objects.

Organisations such as NASA keep track of lots of items of space debris, many as
15   small as 1 cm, but the very tiniest pieces can't be monitored due to their unpredictable orbits and sheer number. This is a problem, since debris orbiting Earth, regardless of its size, travels at extremely high speeds. This means impacts from even the smallest particles can be destructive. The window of a space shuttle had to be replaced after a minute piece of debris collided with it. After analysis, scientists were surprised to find
20   this measurable damage was caused by nothing more than a fleck of paint.

Collisions can be avoided if objects in space can be manoeuvred, but if the density of space debris increases much further, the risks posed to space exploration will be great. The consensus, therefore, is that there must be some intervention to ensure the problem is mitigated. Ingenious ideas, currently in their planning stages, include
25   dispatching state-of-the-art craft to space which are capable of collecting debris, or using lasers to encourage objects to fall out of orbit and towards Earth.

1. Since when has artificial space debris been amassing around Earth?

   A   Since the beginning of the universe

   B   In the last 50 years

   C   Since the beginning of the Space Age

   D   Since 2009

2. Which of the following items is not classed as space debris?

   A   Operational satellites

   B   Fragments of old space craft

   C   Naturally-occurring rocks in space

   D   Parts of rockets which are out-of-service

3. Which of the following statements is true?

   A   Exactly 170,000,000 pieces of artificial space debris are orbiting Earth.

   B   Only small pieces of shrapnel are categorised as space debris.

   C   Scientists have measured exactly the quantity of space debris around Earth.

   D   Scientists have analysed the size of pieces of space debris.

4. How large is the majority of space debris orbiting Earth?

   A   Over ten centimetres in width

   B   Under one centimetre across

   C   Between one and ten centimetres across

   D   The size of a small satellite

TURN OVER ➡

5. Which of the following statements best describes Iridium 33?

  A   A decommissioned Russian satellite.

  B   A communications network in America.

  C   A notable collision between space debris.

  D   An American satellite used for transmissions.

6. According to the text, what was the main problem caused by the 2009 collision?

  A   The amount of space debris orbiting Earth was increased.

  B   Communications were disrupted on Earth.

  C   Nobody knows what happened to the debris shards after the collision.

  D   The orbit of the Russian satellite needed to be altered.

7. Which of the following are reasons why NASA is unable to track small space debris?

  1.   Small objects travel too fast to be monitored.

  2.   The paths that small objects take in orbit are hard to forecast.

  3.   The number of small pieces of debris has become too great.

  4.   Small objects orbit Earth too far away, unlike larger ones which orbit nearer.

  A   1 and 2

  B   1 and 3

  C   2 and 3

  D   2, 3 and 4

8. According to the text, what "surprised" scientists in line 19?

  A   That space debris contained objects as small as a fleck of paint.

  B   That a fleck of paint was intact after colliding with a space shuttle.

  C   That the windows of space shuttles are so fragile.

  D   That incredibly small items of space debris can cause noticeable damage.

9. According to the text, which of the following best describes the opinion of scientists concerning space debris?

A   Steps need to be taken to reduce the amount of space debris.

B   Space exploration needs to be halted until space debris is eliminated.

C   Objects that are vulnerable to damage caused by space debris need to be redesigned.

D   Craft need to be built so they can be manoeuvred faster to avoid collisions.

10. Which of the following statements must be false?

A   It has been agreed that the issue of space debris needs to be tackled.

B   Early models of debris-capturing spacecraft are being designed by scientists.

C   Space debris can be removed from orbit by causing it to fall towards Earth.

D   Lasers are currently used to dislodge items of space debris from their orbits.

11. Which of the following words best describes scientists' ideas about how to remove space debris?

A   Innovative

B   Logical

C   Controversial

D   Convoluted

12. What does "functional" mean (line 9)?

A   Essential

B   Creditable

C   Indispensable

D   Usable

END OF TEST

/ 12

Time for a break! This puzzle is a great way to practise your **word-making** skills.

Travels Through Time

Nine scientists have built a time machine so they can visit a famous historical figure. Below is a statement from each scientist. The incomplete adjectives next to each statement describe how each scientist is feeling. Use each statement to complete the adjectives. The letters in the blue boxes will spell out the identity of the historical figure they're visiting.

Leonardo: "I'm certain that the machine will work."   ☐ O N ☐ ☐ D ☐ N ☐

Albert: "What if the time machine breaks mid-flight?"   F ☐ R F ☐ ☐

Marie: "I can't wait for the adventures that we'll have!"   ☐ ☐ C I ☐ E ☐

Louis: "We shouldn't go anywhere too dangerous."   ☐ A U ☐ ☐ U S

Isaac: "I'm thrilled with what we've achieved in building the machine."   ☐ ☐ ☐ O ☐ D

Ada: "I'm still in shock that we got the machine to work."   A ☐ Z D

René: "I don't know whether we should use the machine."   H E ☐ ☐ ☐ ☐ T

Erwin: "I'm outraged I don't get to choose when we travel to."   ☐ U ☐ I O ☐ ☐

Niels: "I am so emotional I think I might cry."   T E ☐ ☐ ☐ L

The name of the historical figure is: ___ ___ ___ ___ ___ ___ ___ ___ ___

VCXPD2F1